TURN
BLIND EYES

Carel Press Hit Scripts

A play about bullying

by

Ian McCormack

with music by Tim Eden and Jeanette Merrifield

CONTENTS

Published by: Carel Press Ltd, 4 Hewson Street, Carlisle, CA2 5AU

Tel 01228 538928. Fax 591816

info@carelpress.co.uk

www.carelpress.co.uk

© Ian McCormack 1995

Music composed by Tim Eden and Jeanette Merrifield

Music typeset by Penny Stirling

Reprinted 1996, 2001

Printed by Ashford Colour Press, Gosport

Cover photograph: Howard Barlow

Cover design: Arthur Procter

PERFORMANCE

For permission to give a public performance of this play, please contact Carel Press.
No fee will be charged for a performance in an educational, charitable or youth
institution unless an admission charge is made, however, permission is still required.

ENVIRONMENTAL INFORMATION

The book is printed on 100% recycled paper which is made entirely from printed
waste, and is not re-bleached. Using recycled paper saves trees, water and energy, and
reduces air pollution and landfill.

British Library Cataloguing in Publication Data

McCormack, Ian

Turning Blind Eyes: a play about bullying

1. Title 11. Series

822

ISBN 1872365 21 3

TURNING BLIND EYES

Characters

The Tipman Household:

Mum (Mrs Tipman)
Gran (Mrs Tipman's mother)
Jeff Tipman, aged 15
Neil Tipman, aged 20-21
Dad (Mr Tipman)

The Morris Household:

* **Moz** (Christopher Morris), aged 16
Monica, late twenties/early thirties

The Gang:

Janet
Jayne
Henny
Ding

The Staff:

Denis Kershaw
Bev Hardman
* **Mr Myers**

The Pupils:

Richardson
Ben
Mark
Gillian
David
Sandra
Caroline

* See casting notes p 92

Notes for the reader
The text of the play has been prepared for ease of reading thus only the essential stage directions are included. More detailed information can be found under production notes p90 and in the Turning Blind Eyes Performance Pack, available from the publishers. The songs have been included within the text because their lyrics provide additional commentary and reflection on the action.

The performance opens with two contrasting songs.

Back to school - the full cast

Stand up, sit down, turn round, silence, late marks, ticks and crosses
May the wrath of teachers fall on you if you don't learn who the boss is.

It's an age away that July day since we left this dump for summer
Now we've left the fun in the summer sun,
September, what a bummer.

On the Sunday night get your school things right
And be in bed by ten thirty.
You'll have spent an hour in the bath or shower,
Well you mustn't go there dirty.

Books and bags and bikes and bells and pencils, pens and paper
Get the school rules right, keep your ties tied tight.
Cor blimey what a caper.

So it's out at eight, 'cos you can't be late, with your hair combed neat and tidy.
For that living hell that's controlled by bells.
Oh, let it soon be Friday.

And you're there by nine and the day's kept fine,
But morale's already sagging.
Not a lesson learned or a page been turned,
But the day's already dragging.

Classwork, coursework, bookwork, homework, pass marks, fails and credits.
You've made it, prayed it, measured it, weighed it, worked it out and read it.

So the learning starts and it breaks your hearts,
All that discipline and writing.
In the great outdoors there are fewer bores,
And it all seems more exciting.

But the years fly by and you heave a sigh
For your school days and the laughter
And you feel quite sad 'cos they weren't so bad,
But you didn't know till after.

It's an age away that July day since we left this dump for summer.
Now we've left the fun in the summer sun,
September, what a bummer.

Stand up, sit down, turn round, silence, late marks, ticks and crosses
May the wrath of teachers fall on you if you don't learn who the boss is.

Mum's Song

There's no time for a rehearsal
The spotlight's on right from the start.
There's no prompter if you stumble,
You just have to play your part.

Don't go looking for the actors,
You're director, cast and crew.
You're the one who makes the ground plan,
You're the one who gives the cues.

In the lead role of a parent.
The greatest part you'll ever play,
Your only encore is the lifetime,
That your children take away.

Act 1

Scene 1

The action moves between the Tipman house and the Morris house. There is little apparent difference between the two. In the Tipman home Mum is preparing breakfast, setting the table etc. She turns off the TV and shouts upstairs.

Mum: Is there anyone there? Halloooo. Earth to Planet Zog are you receiving me?

Jeff: *(From upstairs)* What?

Mum: Never mind what, get up or there'll be trouble. *(Mum returns to preparation of breakfast.)*

(Evelyn, usually just called Gran, enters from upstairs - Mum obviously thinks it's the person she called. She doesn't turn around.)

Mum: Oh you made it then? Anyone would think I was running a hotel here. I'm like an alarm clock on legs. First it's your dad, then you, then our Neil and then there's your grandma. She'll be out to the world for another two hours, then she'll want breakfast and I can't trust her, I can't trust any of you. At least she's got an excuse.

Gran: Being a bit daft in the head you mean?

Mum: *(Shocked)* Mum! *(She's lost for words.)* It's you ......

Gran: It better had be or I've put the wrong teeth in

Mum: No, No. *(Trying to get out of it)* I meant not going to work, not needing to get up and ...

Gran: *(Knowingly)* I know what you meant, I'm not that stupid ..... yet.

(There's a noise of someone descending the stairs, Mum is glad of the distraction.)

Mum: Oh! Movement at last. *(Cynically)* He must have needed the toilet.

(Her elder son enters. He is wearing jeans and a sweatshirt which he has pulled up over his head.)

Neil: Greetings from Planet Zog.

Mum: Oh it's you. *(She is clearly unimpressed.)*

Neil: We can control you earthmen!

Mum: Don't be stupid Neil. You can't even control yourself. What are you doing here?

Neil: I live here Mother.

Mum: *(Coldly)* Not for much longer or so you tell me.

Neil: Don't start that again.

Mum: Have you seen anything of our Jeff? I must have called him a dozen times

Neil: *(Heavily sarcastic)* Really Mother? I didn't hear.

The action in the Tipman house freezes and attention switches to the lounge of Moz's house. The TV is on. Monica is lying on the couch reading a 'True Love' magazine. She is wearing a dressing gown. She is clearly not old enough to be the mother of a 16 year old. Chris Morris, Moz to his friends, enters. He is 16 years old, naked from the waist up and is finishing a bowl of cereal. He puts the bowl on the coffee table and Monica turns off the TV before he speaks.

Moz: *(Taking the shirt from the ironing board.)* Bloody hell, Monica, I thought you'd ironed this.

Monica: *(Not looking up)* I have ironed it, and don't swear.

Moz: It's full of creases. *(He puts the shirt on during the following dialogue.)*

Monica: Well it'll have to do. It's not my job to do the ironing around here.

Moz: No, we know what your job is.

Monica: *(Stops reading and is clearly annoyed.)* Just watch what you're saying. Just remember who you're talking to.

Moz: *(Undeterred)* That's the trouble, remembering. The old fellah has that many girl friends round.

Monica: Don't think you can wind me up, *(he clearly has)* you little .....

Moz: *(Pleased with his success.)* Now, now, 'No knickers' - calm down.

Monica: Monica, the name's Monica.

Moz: Course it is!! I knew it had *something* to do with knickers.

Monica: *(Throws his coat at him.)* Here take this and get out. There's some money from your dad there for your dinner. He's left some extra so you can get a new pen.

Moz: Pen? I don't need a pen for school but I'll have the money.

Monica: *(Insistent)* Your dad says you're to buy a pen.

Moz: *(Right up to her and equally insistent.)* And I say no. Besides, if I need a pen I'll get one off the lads.

(Moz begins brushing his hair.)

Monica: You really do fancy yourself don't you? You really think you're something, bossing all your mates around. You know what I'd do to you?

Moz: You wouldn't do anything because you're not my Mum, you're nobody. So shut it! *(Moz exits.)*

We return to the Tipman household. Neil and Gran are seated. Mum is clearly agitated and crosses towards the door.

Mum: *(Shouting)* Right, that does it, he's going to be late. Jeff! Jeff!

(As she reaches the door he enters before she can say more. Jeff is dressed but belt, shirt, tie etc are not fastened.)

Jeff: I'm here, what do you want?

Mum: You know very well what I want. It's school today and you're going to be late.

Jeff: I don't feel well. My stomach's .....

Mum: Don't start again, Jeff, there's nothing wrong with you. *(Touches his forehead.)* You seem right as rain to me.

Jeff: My throat's sore as well.

Mum: I thought we'd finished all this last year. I thought it was all sorted. It's every school day alike.

Jeff: And I've got earache. *(He sits at the table.)*

Mum: Jeff it's a new year. You've got new teachers and nothing to worry about. Now make your mind up. Go to school on your own or I'll take you in personally one of these days and I'll have you to the education psychiatrist as well. You're not right in the head you. All this fuss about school - now get some breakfast.

(Jeff reaches for the cereal packet, as he does Gran takes his hand and squeezes it lovingly.)

2 The school yard

First day after the Summer break. The teachers, Mr Kershaw and Miss Hardman, are supervising the yard. Children are involved in games, conversation and general schoolyard activities.

Ben: Morning, Miss.

Miss Hardman: Morning, Ben.

Mr Kershaw: God, this term's dragging.

Miss Hardman: Oh Denis, for heaven's sake, the bell's not even gone yet.

Mr Kershaw: It doesn't have to. Can't you just feel it? Look at them, like a bunch of animals. We've been back ten minutes and it seems like a month.

(*Attracted by a child kicking a drink can - he reacts viciously.*)

Pick that up and put it in a bin, lad. Where do you think you are?

Miss Hardman: Good old Hunter, back where he left off - hope he cleans his teeth this year.

Mr Kershaw: There you are, you're doing it now.

Miss Hardman: Not as bad as you.

Mr Kershaw: Do you know, I really thought about not coming back this time. We got really settled.

Miss Hardman: Where did you go?

Mr Kershaw: France again, go every year. Took the caravan.

Miss Hardman: Don't you get fed up, all that driving?

Mr Kershaw: No. Get your toe down it's no problem. Stick in one lane and bugger the rest of them. One good thing about joining the E.C. - taught those Frogs what a good road is. We just go straight down the A10 to Bordeaux and we're virtually there. Mind you *they* can't drive to save their lives. Maniacs all of them.

Miss Hardman: Then you just stay put in the one place?

Mr Kershaw: Wouldn't dream of moving. Get the old umbrella over the table, set up the barbecue, can't beat it. Feet up, plenty of plonk and Robert's your Uncle.

Miss Hardman: What about Gaynor?

Mr Kershaw: Loves it!! Would not change - well she's got everything there. There's a fridge in the caravan, good cooker and I got her a hoover this year, runs off the battery, so even cleaning is easy.

Miss Hardman: *(Clearly taken aback.)* Has it never .....?

(Mr Kershaw sees two lads fooling around and cuts across Miss Hardman.)

Mr Kershaw: You two!

(Boys give a 'What us?' expression.)

Yes, you two, you little worms. Get back under your stones and stop messing about.

(To Miss Hardman) Morons. Anyway, where did you go?

Miss Hardman: I just took a fortnight at the beginning.

Mr Kershaw: I? What's all this, I? You can't kid me, you went with that fellah who brought you to the staff 'do'. Des, wasn't it?

Miss Hardman: Well, as a matter of fact .....

Mr Kershaw: You! You there! Come here.

(He is talking to Moz who has entered, surrounded by a group of friends.)

Come here I said.

(Moz goes to him, carrying his jacket, but looking quite smart. He is clearly provoked by Mr Kershaw's attentions.)

What's your name lad?

Moz: Moz!

Mr Kershaw:	What do you mean 'Moz'? I want your proper name and say 'Sir' when you speak to me.
Moz:	Morris, Sir, Chris Morris, Sir!
	(He spits out the word 'Sir'.)
Mr Kershaw:	Well get your jacket on Morris and where's your tie?
Moz:	In my bag. *(Pause)*
Mr Kershaw:	Sir!
Moz:	Sir.
Mr Kershaw:	Well, get it round your neck and show it to me after assembly. Look at the state of you. You've not been back five minutes and you're in trouble already. On your way and see me later.
Miss Hardman:	You knew his name then, didn't you?
Mr Kershaw:	*(Smugly)* Course I did, but it does no harm to make them squirm. *(Leering)* Anyway, never mind changing the subject, you were telling me about your holiday with dangerous Des.
Miss Hardman:	As a matter of fact we had a fortnight in Greece.
Mr Kershaw:	Greece eh? Very nice. Sun, sea, sand and se ..... I bet Des had some fun on those topless beaches. I've never actually been to Greece. You must bring in your photos.
Miss Hardman:	Oh I'm not very good at taking pictures. I'm sure an expert like you would find them very underexposed. If you'll excuse me.
	(She leaves Mr Kershaw trying to decide whether he has received an insult or a compliment and drifts across to a group of pupils.)

One way to treat the kids

(Mr Kershaw begins to sing. Miss Hardman joins later verses).

Mr Kershaw:

There's only one way to treat the kids to get the message through,
Knock them about and treat them rough to teach them just who's who.

We send them off to school these days, it's discipline they lack.
You, stand up straight, chin in, chest out, and keep your
    shoulders back.

The worst day's work we ever did was take away the cane,
It teaches lessons and leaves them taught, there's nothing wrong
    with pain.
We've let this country's standards slip, we're on the downward
    track.
You, stand up straight, chin in, chest out, and keep your
    shoulders back.

A quick backhander does the trick, it shows them wrong from
    right.
Don't waste your time with shades of grey, the issue's black and
    white.
Don't spare the rod, you'll spoil the child, and things will just get
    slack.
You, stand up straight, chin in, chest out, and keep your
    shoulders back.

Miss Hardman

Isn't it wonderful being so strong?
When you talk without thinking then nothing seems wrong.
By twisting and bruising to force home your view,
Fear is the message that really gets through.

So you stand over there with your South of France tan,
A latter day link with Neanderthal Man.
But even with your mind it must become clear
You're not winning friends but engendering fear.

Plenty of people have different views
So once in a while why not stand in their shoes?
There's no great achievement in being born big
And no-one admires a chauvinist pig.

*(Miss Hardman and Mr Kershaw repeat their first verses
simultaneously. They are literally singing against each other.)*

*(Miss Hardman looks with disdain at Mr Kershaw and exits. Mr
Kershaw looks after her then exits himself, taking a child by the
ear. Moz and his gang stare after Mr Kershaw.)*

Moz:	Look at him, the dog, he really fancies her. Dirty old man.
Ding:	She's a bit fit though, isn't she?
Janet:	Well don't get excited, 'cos she wouldn't fancy you.
Ding:	*(A little taken aback)* How do you know?
Jayne:	'Cos no-one fancies you Ding.
Ding:	I pulled on Saturday - that girl from St Marks.
Janet:	Ooh, they taking in blind pupils now, then?
Ding:	*(To Jayne)* You saw her, Jayne, didn't you?
Moz:	Shut up Ding and give us your tie.
Ding:	What?
Moz:	Your tie, give it me.
Ding:	What for?
Moz:	You heard Kershaw - I've got to have one for after assembly.
Ding:	What about me?
Moz:	Get another! *(Moves towards him.)*
Ding:	*(Hastily taking off his tie.)* Alright, alright, here.
	(Gives him the tie - Moz takes it without thanks.)
Ding:	*(Shouts another pupil close by.)* Hey, Henny, come here.
Henny:	What's up with you?
Ding:	Give us your tie.
Henny:	What?
Ding:	Your tie, give it us.
Henny:	Why?

Ding: Cos I need one and Moz's got mine.

          (Henny looks at Moz for guidance.)

Moz: Give it him then.

          (He gives it.)

Ding: You can get another, you'll be alright.

Moz: Here you go then, here's your man.

          (Jeff has entered hoping not to be seen.)

Jayne: Aw, not him again, Moz, not Tipman, it's not fair.

Moz: Shut up! Janet, go with her and get him.

          (The three boys watch as they approach Jeff.)

Janet: *(Walks right up to Jeff and looks in his face.)* Hello, Jeff, your acne's got better hasn't it?

          (Jeff turns away, Janet pulls his face back.)

          Still got a few blackheads here and there, though.

          (Jeff puts his hand to his face.)

Jayne: Moz wants you.

Jeff: *(Nervously)* I'm alright here.

Janet: I could tell him that.

          (Jeff looks alarmed.)

Jayne: He'll only beat you up, you might as well go.

          (The girls part and Jeff walks between them towards Moz, Ding and Henny. The girls follow him.)

Jeff: I've got no money, I'm bringing sandwiches this term.

Moz: Who said anything about money? *(Pleasantly)* We're just glad to see you, aren't we everyone?

Chorus: Yes, course we are.

Moz: (*Change of tone to threatening.*) Give Henny your tie.

Jeff: What for?

Moz: Never mind what for, give it him!

Jeff: But I'll get done.

Moz: (*Grabs Jeff's face between thumb and fingers.*) And you'll get smacked by me if you don't, so give it him.

(*Jeff removes his tie, the gang laugh and Henny begins to put it on.*)

Henny: Thanks Jeff.

(*Moz releases him.*)

Ding: (*Pushes him.*) Push off Tipman

Moz: Oh and Tipman -

Jeff: Yeah?

(*Mr Myers, another teacher, enters unseen.*)

Moz: Good idea that, changing to butties. Usually get peckish at break - so bring them out - OK?

Jeff: (*Resignedly*) Yes, Moz.

(*Mr Myers approaches Jeff.*)

Jayne: (*Only half reproachfully.*) You're not going to nick his dinner are you?

Moz: No. Well, not all of it.

Jayne: (*Laughing*) You're a rat.

Moz: That's why you think I'm gorgeous innit?

(*He grabs Jayne.*)

Jayne: Yes, but . . .

(He tries to kiss her.)

Get off, not now.

Ding: It was better when he brought dinner money.

Henny: Yeah, you can't buy fags with a cheese butty.

Moz: Henny, shut it, you're a plonker. When we eat his butties, he'll have to start bringing money as well.

Ding: Then we have it.

Moz: Very good Ding!

Janet: *(To Jayne)* What's it like having a clever boyfriend?

               (In another part of the playground Mr Myers is already in conversation with Jeff)

Mr Myers: I'm not stupid you know, something's going on. It was going on last term as well.

Jeff: Really, Sir, there's nothing. They're my mates, we were joking.

Mr Myers: People like that don't go away, you know.

Jeff: They're my mates, Sir.

Mr Myers: They're looking after your tie as a favour then?

Jeff: *(Hand goes to his neck.)*

               No Sir, it wasn't mine, I've lost mine.

               (School bell rings.)

Mr Myers: I'm going to get to the bottom of this. I've got you next lesson.

Jeff: Please Sir, don't say anything. My Mum'll get me a new tie - honest.

               (Mr Myers turns away and blows his whistle.)

3 A classroom.

It is towards the end of a History lesson. A pupil is reading an extract about Nazi Germany.

Mark: By this time economic collapse was virtually complete. Fortunes had been lost and the infrastructure destroyed to an extent that recovery seemed impossible. It is true that there were still people with lots of money. Indeed there were those who carried thousands of marks around in a suitcase but in reality such an amount would barely have purchased a loaf of bread. *(He looks to the teacher.)*

Mr Myers: Thanks Mark. So, by now you should all be fairly clear that the German people were desperate for change and resentful of those other countries which they felt were to blame for their situation. So, along comes the man you've been waiting for, our Adolph. But before we carry on, let's go back. We know his background and his early years, but what did he think? David, read out that passage I gave you.

David: Our motto shall be - if you will not be a true German I will bash your skull in.

Mr Myers: And Gillian, the other one please.

Gillian: Always, before God and the world, the stronger has the right to carry through what he wills. History proves he who has not the strength, doesn't benefit at all from being 'in the right'. The whole world of nature is a mighty struggle between strength and weakness - an eternal victory of the strong over the weak - Hitler 1923.

Mr Myers: Thank you Gillian. *(Thoughtfully, almost wistfully)* Before God and the world. So we have ..... *(Moz enters.)*

Mr Myers: Ah, nice of you to drop in, Christopher.

Moz: I had to see Kershaw.

Mr Myers: *Mr* Kershaw. That was forty minutes ago, the lesson's nearly over.

Moz: He likes to keep you waiting.

Mr Myers: Clearly. Still, never mind, you can give Jeff Tipman his tie back now, can't you?

Moz: I've not got his tie. Ask him. Ask anyone.

Mr Myers: Oh I will, Morris, I will, and I'm sure they'll support you.

Moz: Yeah, because it's the truth.

Mr Myers: Before God and the world no doubt. *(The bell rings.)* Alright, off
                    you go - Tipman, you stay behind.

                    *(As the class exits Ding and Henny hit Jeff in the back. Janet,
                    Jayne and Moz remain by the door, Jeff is standing separately.)*

Mr Myers: What do you want Morris?

Moz: I'm waiting for my mate Jeff. *(Stares at him.)*

Mr Myers: Well I'm sure he can manage without you. *(Moz leaves.)*

Mr Myers: *(To the girls.)* And you two, off you go.

Janet: We've got to see Jeff.

Jayne: He's meeting us at break for this thing.

Janet: For food studies, sort of planning a packed lunch. *(They both
                    giggle.)*

Mr Myers: Well, he'll see you outside. *(To Jeff)* What's going on?

Jeff: *(Declaring innocence)* Nothing Sir, really. *(Starts to leave.)* Can I
                    go out to my mates now, Sir?

Mr Myers: They're not really your mates, Jeff.

Jeff: They'll be waiting.

Mr Myers: And if I gave you a detention for having no tie?

Jeff: I'd have to do it, Sir. Please, can I go?

Mr Myers: Just tell me the truth, I'll sort it out.

Jeff: There's nothing, Sir, really. Can I .....

Mr Myers: *(Annoyed, cuts across him.)* Yes, go. *(He watches Jeff leave and
                    shakes his head)*

4 Breaktime

Outside; the pupils are grouped around.

Henny: He'd better keep his mouth shut.

Ding: He will, you've nothing to worry about.

Henny: It's alright for you, it's me that's got his tie.

Moz: Yeah, a poxy tie, Henny, it's not the crown jewels. Anyway, Myers thinks I took it, so you're safe.

Henny: But what if he says something?

Moz: He won't, he never has before, he's too scared.

     (Janet and Jayne arrive.)

Jayne: He's coming.

Janet: He never said anything, Moz, we listened.

Moz: Tell him. *(Indicates Henny)* I was never worried. *(Henny shrugs out of bravado.)*

Ding: Hope it's cheese with pickle.

Henny: What?

Ding: On his butties, we're having them aren't we?

Moz: Course we are. Just to remind him what the score is. *(Jeff has entered and is trying to be anonymous.)*

Janet: There he is.

Moz: Oi, shit heap, come here! *(Jeff doesn't react.)* Shit heap, come here. *(No reaction)* He's deaf.

     (The rest of the gang take up the call rather like calling a dog, they whistle as well to attract Jeff.)

     Alright, go and get him.

(Ding and Henny drag Jeff over. They are rough, twisting his arm and kicking him. They stop in front of Moz who grabs Jeff's hair.)

Why don't you come when I call you?

Jeff: *(In pain)* I didn't hear you.

Ding: *(Hits him backhanded in the stomach.)* Well we were all shouting.

Janet: What were you doing, squeezing your spots? *(Laughter)*

Moz: *(Takes Jeff's fingers so he can bend them back.)* It's time for a lesson so you remember your name - what is it? *(He bends his fingers.)* Quickly!

Jeff: Tipman, Jeff Tipman.

Moz: Tipman that's right. *(Bends finger, Jeff screams.)* Now a tip is like you Jeffrey - a load of rubbish. So you are a Tip man - a load of rubbish, a shit heap. Understand? *(Twists fingers.)*

Jeff: Yes

Moz: Who are you then?

Jeff: *(Who has now sunk to his knees.)* Shit heap.

Moz: Good. Goo-ood!

Jayne: Careful Moz, don't bust his fingers again.

Moz: *(Lets go.)* I won't. *(He kicks Jeff.)* Shit heap - give us your butties. *(Jeff does and they eat them. The others crowd Jeff and begin to prod him giving variations on shit heap - cess pit - scumbag - dustbin, etc.)*

Playground Song

Gang: Think of the buzz when they squirm with pain.
You're ten feet tall, people know your name.
You're in control, you're high on power,
Each and every day, each and every hour.

Treading on toes or twisting an arm.
It's good honest fun, can't do any harm.
It isn't a question of right over wrong,
This world's not for weaklings, this world's for the strong.

Jeff: How can this be happening in such a public place?
Of all the people standing by, none looks me in the face.
They turn away, or laugh along and try not to offend,
Looking after number one's the only thing that matters in the end.

Don't close your eyes, don't close your ears because it isn't you.
Your conspiracy of silence just makes you guilty too.
Give me back my freedom from the pain I have to hide.
I shouldn't have to undergo this shame I feel inside.

The Crowd: We didn't see nothing, it's safer that way.
We've nothing to offer, we've nothing to say.
It's another misfortune, there's nothing to do.
But to cast your eyes downwards and be glad it's not you.

(Mr Myers enters - convinced there's an incident. The crowd closes round Jeff and conceals him.)

Mr Myers: What's going on here? *(Silence)* Well? Morris, what's going on?

Moz: Why are you always picking on me? I'm just eating my butties.

Mr Myers: And that brings the crowds in does it?

Moz: *(Clearly sarcastic)* I'm a very interesting person.

Mr Myers: Watch it, Morris.

Jayne: It was a bet, we were seeing how fast he could eat a cheese butty.

Mr Myers: *(Clearly disappointed)* I thought more of you Jayne. Offering excuses for the likes of him, my God.

Henny: Yeah it was a bet, that's right.

Mr Myers: Shut up Henfield - Morris over there, out of the way. *(Sends Morris away. He turns to the crowd.)* Right you lot, what was going on?

(The crowds response is to sing the 'We didn't see nothing' chorus from playground song. Mr Myers sings verses from his song in reply.)

Mr Myers: Is freedom for some too hard to bear?
They parcel up land, they bottle the air,
They take over countries, they hoard all the food,
And nurture the myth that power makes good,
That hunger and fear can govern a land,
And questions be answered by clenching a hand,
By driving in knuckles, by splitting of skin,
Regardless of justice, the mighty must win.

So like the wise monkeys, with nothing to say,
We stand there in silence while evil holds sway.

Some world where religion or colour of skin
Are taunted, are beaten, are seen as a sin.
A world where full knowledge will overtake youth,
When child becomes adult and sees that the truth
Is of leaders who rule but no longer serve
And of others around us who simply won't swerve
From their passion for money, their passion for gain,
Whose worth is best felt when inflicting a pain.

But like the wise monkeys, with nothing to say,
We stand there in silence while evil holds sway.

Mr Myers: Alright, please yourselves. Morris. *(Moz comes up to him.)* I want you anyway, Mr Kershaw says he only saw you for two minutes after assembly. You were 40 minutes late for my lesson.

Moz: But, Sir.

Mr Myers: But nothing. You're in detention next Tuesday. Collect the form from the staff room. *(Turns to leave.)* And the rest of you clear off. *(Exits)*

(Whilst Mr Myers is distracted, clearing the crowd, the gang push Jeff forward.)

Moz: *(To Jeff)* This is your fault shit heap. He's only narked because he doesn't know what's happening. *(Thumps Jeff in stomach, he crumples. Mr Kershaw arrives as this is happening but sees none of the violence.)*

Mr Kershaw: *(To Mr Myers)* Alright? What's going on? *(To Jeff)* You push off. *(Exit Jeff.)*

Mr Myers: Fighting, at least I think so.

Mr Kershaw: No bodies lying around. Can't have been too serious.

Mr Myers: Morris at the centre I'm sure.

Mr Kershaw: Centre of what? *(To stragglers)* Get a move on you idiots!

Mr Myers: Bullying, violence.

Mr Kershaw: *(Patronising)* Look, take it from me, don't get too involved. If it was that serious we'd know about it. Things like this happen everyday. It's something and nothing.

Mr Myers: I hope you're right.

5 By the sweet shop

Pupils are going home. Moz is waiting. Ding and Henny arrive with Jeff. They have forced him to come.

Ding: Look what we've got.

Henny: Found him in the toilets.

Moz: Well, well, you weren't hiding by any chance were you?

Jeff: No Moz.

Moz: I'm in a hurry so we'll get straight to the point.

Jeff: I never meant to get you in trouble, I didn't know Myers was coming. I hid while he was there, I didn't say anything.

Moz: Precisely.

Henny: Me and Jayne had to make the excuses.

Ding: 'Cos you kept your mouth shut. You could have told him there was no bother.

Henny: But now Moz's got a detention. So say you're sorry.

Jeff: Sorry Moz.

Ding: Really sorry.

Henny: Kiss his feet!

                 (Throughout this scene Ding and Henny have held Jeff by the wrists with their other hand on his elbow. Moz stares in front impassively. Ding and Henny now force Jeff to his knees and bend him down to Moz's shoes.)

Moz: *(Dragging Jeff up by the hair, he holds his face really close.)* Compensation, that's what we want. Never mind slavering all over my shoes. What are you going to pay?

Jeff: I've given you my butties, I've had no dinner today. Isn't that enough?

Moz: No it's not enough.

Henny: You can't buy fags with cheese butties.

Ding: Then there's the inconvenience.

Moz: Five quid.

Jeff: Five quid. I can't. I haven't got it.

Moz: Then get it for tomorrow.

Jeff: I can't, my Mum'll know.

Moz: End of the week, you've got till Friday.

Jeff: Please Moz, I'll bring more butties. I got a sweatshirt for my birthday, you can have that.

Moz: Five quid, shit heap. *(Throws him to the floor and is about to kick him when Jayne and Janet arrive.)*

Jayne: Moz! *(Moz stops short of kicking.)* I thought you were meeting me.

Moz: I am, we were just having a bit of fun.

Jayne: Let him go, it's getting boring. *(She picks up Jeff.)* Jeffrey's like us. *(Very patronising.)* He's got to get home, haven't you chuck? *(Straightens his hair.)*

Janet:	Yeah, he's got to go home and squeeze his blackheads. *(Laughs)*
Jayne:	Run along now Jeffrey. *(Jeff runs away.)* *(Sarcastically to herself)* Thanks Jayne. Thanks very much.
Ding:	Why did you do that? We were having fun.
Henny:	Yeah, you should have seen him kiss Moz's feet.
Jayne:	Shut up you two. Getting Tipman all the time is boring.
Janet:	And we're freezing waiting for you.
Jayne:	Come on, Moz. I thought we were going to yours.
Moz:	OK, come on. See you tonight you two.
Ding & Henny:	See you.
Janet:	Come on boys, you can take me to the bus stop.

6 Moz's house

The room is empty but the TV is on. Moz enters first, looks round quickly, and calls back to Jayne.

Moz:	It's alright. She's gone out. *(Moves underwear etc to one end of couch.)* Sit down. *(Jayne comes in and sits down opposite him.)*
Moz:	Over here, sit with me. *(She goes and joins him.)*
Jayne:	Is this alright? I mean should we be here? They won't mind? *(She is obviously worried.)*
Moz:	'Course they won't. Come here. Give us a kiss.
Jayne:	What if they come in?
Moz:	We're doing nothing bad, c'mon give us a kiss.
	(They are about to kiss when Monica enters. Jayne jumps up embarrassed. Moz is clearly annoyed.)

Moz: Oh for Pete's sake, what do you want?

Monica: Don't be so cheeky. It suits alright when you want your shirts washing. *(To Jayne.)* Hello love, what's your name?

Jayne: *(Meekly)* Jayne.

Monica: Well with a bit of luck you'll pack him in before it does too much harm.

Moz: Just shut it you or I'll .....

Monica: You'll what? Don't threaten me lad, I'm not afraid of you. *(Moz looks deflated.)* Do you want a drink love?

Moz: No she doesn't, she wants to be left alone so get lost.

Monica: I've told you once. Any more and I'll tell your dad.

Moz: Dad! When are you going to see him? He's never here.

Monica: He's never here 'cos he's keeping this house for you. And when he is here you're swanning off out with your so-called mates.

Moz: Well perhaps you could arrange an appointment for me. You seem to do everything else for him.

Monica: Right, that's it, I've had enough. You're so selfish. Only you matter. Me, me, me, all the time. You might not have had it easy but neither has your dad. Why don't you think of someone else for a change?

Moz: I thought you were going, push off!

Monica: I offered Jayne a drink, and you too if you want one.

Moz: Well we don't, so push off.

Jayne: *(Who has been embarrassed throughout all of this exchange.)* Look, I think I'd better go.

Monica: No, it's alright love, I was going shopping anyway. You stay if you want. *(To Moz)* I suppose no matter how much you hate me you'll still have your tea when I make it. *(Exit)*

Moz: *(Under his breath - he thumps a cushion.)* Bitch.

(There is a long silence during which Jayne just stares at Moz. Finally he feels too uncomfortable and speaks.)

Moz: Stop it.

Jayne: Stop what?

Moz: Looking at me.

Jayne: Why? Feeling guilty?

Moz: *(Indignantly)* No, why should I?

Jayne: You really embarrassed me, talking to Monica like that.

Moz: She deserved it.

Jayne: No she didn't. She was right.

Moz: Go on, take her side then.

Jayne: There you are, you're feeling sorry for yourself now. It's like going out with two different people.

Moz: What do you mean?

Jayne: You. There are times when you can be so kind and a good laugh and then others when you're just horrible.

Moz: *(Defensively)* I'm not horrible. Ask Ding! Ask Henny! Ask anyone. I'm not horrible.

Jayne: Shall I ask Tipman?

Moz: What's he got to do with it? He's just a laugh.

Jayne: Or Monica, shall I ask her?

Moz: She doesn't count.

Jayne: Your dad seems to think so.

Moz: Yeah well ..... *(pause)*

Jayne: It's not her fault you know, ... your Mum dying and everything.

Moz: *(Angry)* I know that. But she's here trying to replace her, and I hate her for it.

Jayne: And your dad, he tries to be here, people have to go to work.

Moz: *(Softening slightly)* I know ..... *(pause)* When my Mum was dying, he never went to work for ages, just visited her every day, all day nearly. Sometimes he stayed all night. Then, near the end, he brought her home. Nursed her. He had to do everything, he washed her, dressed her, even took her to the toilet but she still died *(pause)*. After the funeral he just cried, cried for about two days. Then he just cleared the house, got rid of everything. He even put the pictures of her away in a box. I had to help him put it in the loft. He wanted to burn them but I wouldn't let him. *(Angry and upset.)* She was *my* Mum and you can't just burn her, she was my Mum *(pause)*.

Jayne: Do you think that's why he works so much, to forget?

Moz: Partly, but not just that. After he took all that time off with my Mum we owed a fortune. He never got paid. We nearly lost the house. That's why Monica came. Sort of lodger to help with bills but it didn't stop there .....

Jayne: No.

Moz: She can't replace her you know. She can't come here and replace my Mum.

Jayne: I don't think she wants to.

Moz: *(Emphatically and aggressively.)* Well she can't! *(Pause)* I've never told anyone this, but I still miss her.

Jayne: You don't have .....

Moz: Let me tell you, I want to. When she first died I kept thinking I saw her, I'd see cars outside school and think *(Brightly)* Mum's here! Then I'd remember. The other day in town I thought I saw her. This woman in front of me in Smiths. I reached out to touch her shoulder. I'd nearly done it when she turned round. There was I looking like an idiot and it wasn't my Mum. She thought I was trying to nick her bag. *(Aggressively)* I could have smashed her face in.

Jayne: Stop it, Moz. Stop getting like this.

Moz: Other kids have Mums. You have a Mum, but not me. Even bloody Tipman's got a Mum, but not me. Why can't I be like everyone else?

Jayne: I don't know, it just works out that way.

Moz: Yeah. Well I'm not like everyone else, so they'd better remember. Me, Chris Morris, I'm special. *(He emphasises this and tries to show his superiority - there is quite a long pause.)* Like that Tipman, you said about him. He knows I'm special. *(Laughs)* He might have a Mum but he knows I'm special, the little shit.

Jayne: Moz, I think it's gone too far with him, I think it should stop.

Moz: It's a laugh, I told you, it's just a laugh.

Jayne: He doesn't think so. You broke his fingers last term.

Moz: It was an accident, he knows that. He struggled, he broke them himself.

Jayne: Accident or not, will you stop?

Moz: Stop what?

Jayne: Picking on Tipman, knocking him about.

Moz: He'll think I've gone soft.

Jayne: He won't.

Moz: He will, everyone will.

Jayne: He won't, *they* won't, please just stop.

Moz: I thought you were my girlfriend.

Jayne: I am.

Moz: You're supposed to be on my side.

Jayne: Please. For me.

Moz: *(Softening)* Alright, I'll think about it.

Jayne: *(Kisses him briefly.)* Thanks - I've got to go.

Moz: *(Pulls her back.)* Jayne.

Jayne: What?

Moz: What I said, all that about my Mum, you won't tell anyone will you? Ever?

Jayne: Course not. Got to go. *(Kisses his cheek.)* Bye! *(He looks after her.)*

7 Tipman's house

The TV is on, showing news of a famine. Gran is present from the start of the scene but ignored by the others.

Mum: *(To herself)* Depressing rubbish. *(Turns off the TV.)*

Neil: I was watching that.

Mum: Well you're not now.

Neil: Pardon me for existing.

Mum: I'm having great difficulty doing that at the moment, Neil.

Dad: There's perhaps something else on the other side.

Neil: Here we go. We're off again are we?

Dad: I mean, you know what Channel 4 is like.

Mum: No we're not off again. I just don't want starving people rammed down my throat at tea time when I'm trying to relax.

Dad: I could put the radio on, we never sit and listen these days.

Neil: Typical that is, just typical.

Mum: I beg your pardon? *(Pause)* What did you say?

Neil: I said it's typical.

Dad: I'll go and finish mending that ironing board. *(Exit)*

Mum: And what's that meant to mean?

Neil: It means, Mother, that the television's just the tip of the iceberg.

Mum: Oh I see, I can't even turn off the television without Mr Knowitall sees some vast social significance. No doubt you've some all-encompassing theory on this as well, have you?

Neil: Well, as a matter of fact, I have.

Mum: What a surprise.

Neil: Because it's not just the television, you're the same with everything. When are you going to live life Mother, the way it is, instead of how you'd wish it to be?

Mum: So, it's all me is it? I'm responsible for the famines in Africa am I? And I suppose I'm the one throwing away my life to shack up with a bit of stuff instead of waiting like proper people.

Neil: That's right, Mother, let's get the real issue out in the open.

            (Dad enters to get a screwdriver from the chair arm.)

Dad: Couldn't you just watch a video Neil?

Mum: I thought you were mending the ironing board.

Dad: Yes, I was. *(Sheepishly)* Just getting a screwdriver. *(Exits)*

Neil: Those people in Africa won't go away, you know, just because you turn off the television, any more than I'll change my mind because of your unpleasantness and Angela won't go away because you won't discuss her.

Mother: There's nothing to discuss. You know my views. It's you that causes this unpleasantness not me. All I did was turn off the television.

Neil: While I was watching it. All you did was make snide comments for the past six weeks and grunt and snort and sniff and sigh. Oh, and refuse to take so much as a telephone message for me.

Mum: You've hurt me Neil. You've not had so much as a second thought for my feelings. That's what I find so hard to bear.

Neil: Oh no Mum. I'll tell you what you find so hard to bear. Your dreams. That's what's getting up your nose. Things aren't working out according to the master plan.

Mum: Don't be so stupid.

Neil: No, come on Mum, let's have a look at what's going on here. All
                  I want to do, at the age of 21 nearly, is spend my last twelve
                  months at University living with somebody. With Angela, a girl I
                  happen to love.

Mum: *(With derision)* Hmph.

Neil: Never mind 'Hmph' Mother. Somebody I happen to love,
                  someone who commits the double sin of not being a Catholic,
                  and not being selected by my Mother. I've made a choice,
                  Mother. It may not be the one you wanted but I've made a
                  choice.

Mum: I know very well what you've done.

                  *(Jeff enters, sees what is going on and slumps into a chair. As he
                  does so he turns on the television.)*

Mum: Where have you been till now? You can turn that off. *(He does
                  so and takes a magazine.)*

Neil: That's what gets to you, isn't it? The fact that I've made a choice.
                  Well let me tell you this. The only reason I'm here now is because
                  you wouldn't hear of me applying anywhere else. I've done what
                  you wanted, I've lived at home, I've been to University and whilst
                  I've been there I've changed. I've grown up, Mother. I've got a
                  life of my own. And what gets up your nose Mother, is that one
                  day you're not going to put your best hat on and walk in St
                  Mark's in your posh frock to preside over a wedding planned in
                  exactly the way you've dreamed of. Well I'm very sorry, Mother,
                  but other people live in this world and your dreams are going to
                  have to accommodate them, and if I don't choose to fall in love
                  with the girl of your dreams then you're going to have to put
                  your posh frock on for something else.

Mum: It's nothing to do with posh frocks.

Neil: It's everything to do with posh frock and white dresses and
                  Catholic churches. All the time it's *your* thoughts, and your
                  perceptions and never mind what anyone else thinks. You push
                  it away, you never do more than scratch the surface, everything
                  has to fit your ideas.

Mum: It's not true, any of it. I just want the best for people.

Neil: My dad knows, he doesn't even try to talk now, he just clears off and mends an ironing board.

Mum: Don't start questioning my marriage. Who do you think you are? You aren't even .....

Neil: What about our Jeff?

Jeff: *(Instantly)* Leave me out of it!

Neil: What about last term, all that bother? You wouldn't even go into school.

Jeff: *(Under his breath)* Thank God.

Neil: It'll all blow over, you said.

Mum: Well, it has done. He's at a difficult age is Jeff.

Jeff: Yeah, and going by you two I've not got much chance of growing out of it.

Mum: Don't you be so cheeky. Come in here with a face like a yard of tripe and you think you can interfere in people's discussions.

Neil: There you go again. It's not a discussion, it's an argument. An argument you refuse to listen to.

Mum: Well I can't anymore 'cos I've got the tea to make. You make me sick both of you.

Jeff: Why me?

Mum: Both of you. Insulting me, insulting your father. It's something when you can't express an opinion in your own house without being pilloried for it.

Neil: *(Exasperated)* Mother.

Mother: *(Exit whilst saying this line, pursued by Neil.)* You'll want your tea though won't you? You'll have me as your skivvy, your home help. *(She continues to mutter as she leaves.)*

Neil: Mother will you just stop and listen for one minute?

(There is a long pause.)

(After a few seconds Jeff gets up slowly and creeps to the door. He listens. He creeps back and takes Mum's handbag from the chair and crosses to the table. He takes out the purse. As he is opening it, Gran, whom everyone appears to have forgotten, speaks.)

Gran: I'm still here you know. *(Jeff jumps out of his skin and stuffs the purse back into the bag.)* Forgot me did you, like everyone else? Thought I was a bit of the furniture?

Jeff: No Gran.

Gran: I'm not thick you know. Your Mother thinks I am, but I'm not thick.

Jeff: I didn't say you were.

Gran: Well what are you up to?

Jeff: Nothing.

Gran: Jeff, I asked you a question.

Jeff: *(Pause)* I was looking for my library tickets.

Gran: In your Mother's purse?

Jeff: I thought they might be there.

Gran: Are you short of money?

Jeff: No.

Gran: Have they been at it again?

Jeff: Who?

Gran: I know what's been going on. I can guess even if your Mother can't. Are they picking on you at school?

Jeff: Course not, why would they do that? They're my mates.

Gran: Why were you late home then? And what happened to your shirt?

Jeff: Nothing. It was an accident. I've been talking. *(Annoyed)* God, it's like the Gestapo this is.

Gran: Do they want money, is that it?

Jeff: No Gran, honest. I don't know what you're talking about.

Gran: Well, why did you want your Mum's purse?

Jeff: I've told you, my library tickets, I wanted my library tickets.

Gran: I know what you told me and I'm telling you. You can't pay people like that off. The only thing that works is the truth and that's something you're not telling.

Jeff: Gran, honest.

Gran: Don't use that word if you don't mean it.

(She rises and crosses to the door. She turns back to him.)

And think on, the truth.

(Gran goes out, as she leaves she picks up Mum's bag and takes it with her.)

Jeff: Damn.

(He falls back into a chair.)

8 The Music room

The next day. Jeff enters looking cautious and furtive. He checks around carefully before he comes into the Music Room. There is a keyboard on the table. He toys with the instrument and is about to start playing when he hears his name called. It is Mr Kershaw calling but Jeff thinks it is Moz.

Mr Kershaw: *(Aggressively)* Tipman! Tipman!

(Jeff hides behind the table. Mr Kershaw enters).

Mr Kershaw: I saw you come in, I know you're here. Get out from behind there. *(Jeff comes out reluctantly.)* Now, what are you up to?

Jeff: Sir?

Mr Kershaw: Never mind 'Sir'. What are you up to?

Jeff: Nothing Sir, I came in to play the keyboard Sir.

Mr Kershaw: You were hiding, I saw you, you must be up to something.

Jeff: No Sir, it's just .....

Mr Kershaw: Just what? Come on, out with it.

Jeff: I was hiding Sir, but not from you, I thought you were someone else.

Mr Kershaw: Oh, someone else eh? It's always happening to me. Who did you think it was? Tom Cruise? Jason Donovan?

Jeff: No Sir.

Mr Kershaw: That's right, 'no Sir'. It wasn't anybody because you were up to something and I want to know what.

Jeff: *(Pleading)* Please Sir .....

Mr Kershaw: *(Takes Jeff by the ear.)* Listen lad, let me tell you something .....

                 (He moves Jeff to the back of the classroom and continues to prod, twist and interrogate - Mr Myers and Miss Hardman enter.)

Miss Hardman: Who's Kershaw got his knife into now?

Mr Myers: It looks like Tipman.

Miss Hardman: It is Tipman. He seems to get it all ways. First the kids and then the teachers.

Mr Myers: What do you mean, the kids?

Miss Hardman: You know, Chris Morris and his mob, they're always at him.

Mr Myers: How do you know? That is, I mean can you prove it?

Miss Hardman: Of course I can't prove it. Usual thing. We know who the bullies are but as soon as you ask, everyone clams up. It's not right, but what can you do?

Mr Myers: Well we could make a start with Kershaw at least. Come on. *(They cross to Mr Kershaw.)* Ah Mr Kershaw thank you, thank you so much.

Mr Kershaw: *(Astonished)* Mr Myers, Miss Hardman.

Mr Myers: It's good to know someone cares, we thought Tipman would be locked out, didn't we Miss Hardman?

Miss Hardman: We did, but we shouldn't have worried. Mr Kershaw to the rescue.

Mr Myers: We got delayed you see, couldn't get back to let Jeff here in.

Miss Hardman: Traffic in town. Funnily enough we were talking about you - I was telling Mr Myers about your interest in photography.

Mr Myers: *(Playing along.)* Yes all that technical stuff about exposure and so on - amazing.

Mr Kershaw: *(Embarrassed)* Well, I'll get off, Tipman's here now.

Mr Myers: *(Patronisingly)* Y-e-e-e-s.

Mr Kershaw: I was just checking the rooms you see. Thought he was hiding at first.

Miss Hardman: Glad you spotted him.

Mr Kershaw: Yes, well I'll get off then.

(Mr Kershaw leaves . At the same time, Jeff tries to leave behind the back of Mr Myers and Miss Hardman who are watching Mr Kershaw.)

Mr Myers: Don't sneak off Tipman.

Jeff: Sir?

Mr Myers: What were you doing in here?

Jeff: I just came in, out of the way, to play the keyboard.

Mr Myers: Get on with it then. *(Jeff crosses to the keyboard.)*

Miss Hardman: If anything was going on Jeff, if there was any other reason for being here, you could tell us.

Jeff: There was nothing, Miss.

Miss Hardman: Were you hiding?

Jeff: No, Miss. *(Then as an afterthought.)* Honest.

Mr Myers: Lying doesn't help you know, Jeff. (Silence) I've just got you off the hook with Mr Kershaw. You owe me the truth at least.

Jeff: It is the truth, Sir.

Mr Myers: Just remember, Jeff, the more you keep quiet the easier you make it for them.

Miss Hardman: Don't give us names, just tell us. Is there anything worrying you?

Jeff: No, Miss. *(Emphatically)* Honest.

(He turns to the keyboard, they resignedly turn and leave. Jeff begins to play. Jayne, attracted by the music, enters. For quite a while she listens whilst he plays, unaware of her presence. When she finally speaks he is astonished by her arrival and fearful of whom she has with her.)

Jayne: Hidden talents.

(Jeff panics, switches off the keyboard and backs off quickly.)

Jayne: Don't panic, I'm on my own. *(Jeff tries to look behind her.)*

Jayne: Really, I'm on my own, don't worry. Proper Richard Clayderman, aren't you? *(Jeff says nothing, just looks blank.)*

Jayne: He's a pianist. *(Pause)* Richard Clayderman, my Mum's got his records. *(Pause)* He has long hair ..... and a big smile ..... He's a bit naff really ..... Has the cat got your tongue or something? Only I seem to be doing all the work.

Jeff: Was that a compliment?

Jayne: What? About the cat having your tongue?

Jeff: No, about me being naff like Richard Clayderman.

Jayne: I didn't say that.

Jeff: Very nearly.

Jayne: Well I didn't mean that. I like it, I like the way you play.

Jeff: Has he sent you?

Jayne: Who?

Jeff: You know who. Moz. Has he sent you?

Jayne: Course not. I was passing and I liked the music.

Jeff: Where is he then?

Jayne: I don't know. I was just passing that's all and I heard you so I stopped.

Jeff: I've not got the money.

Jayne: What?

Jeff: The fiver, I've not got the fiver, I can't, my Gran caught me.

Jayne: I'll fix that, don't worry.

Jeff: Oh yeah, what will you do, print some?

Jayne: I'll just talk to him, I'll tell him.

Jeff: Why?

Jayne: What do you mean, why?

Jeff: Why? Why will you tell him? What will you say?

Jayne: I don't know. I'll just say you haven't got it. He'll understand. I'll think of something. Really.

Jeff: But why will you do it for me?

Jayne: 'Cos I like you. You're alright really and you're good on the keyboard.

Jeff: *(Getting embarrassed.)* I'm not, I make loads of mistakes.

Jayne: Do you play it a lot?

Jeff: Quite a lot. It's good when you're on your own. You can lose yourself, imagine.

Jayne: Do you write things, make up your own tunes?

Jeff: Yeah, I've made up loads. That one then, I made that up.

Jayne: Did you, honest?

Jeff: Yeah, I did it for a girl.

Jayne: A girl? You?

Jeff: Yeah, me. It is possible you know.

Jayne: I'm sorry. Did she like it? What did she say?

Jeff: She doesn't really know. She's heard it, once but she's got a boyfriend and I don't think she'd really like me.

Jayne: She might. You're quite cute really.

Jeff: Well it doesn't really matter. I'm not her type.

               (Jeff turns and plays - there is a pause.)

Jayne: Come to the disco.

Jeff: *(Shocked)* What?

Jayne: Tonight, come to the disco.

Jeff: I can't.

Jayne: Why not? For me, come for me.

Jeff: I can't, I've not got the money and Moz .....

Jayne: That's it! I told you I'd think of something. You've been selling tickets, haven't you?

Jeff: Yeah.

Jayne: Well, nick a few. They'd never suspect you and anyway it's not like really stealing, not from school.

Jeff: I don't know, it's .....

Jayne: Look, get the tickets and I'll get you in the gang. I can sort it out.

You could be the gang's fixer. You could get in places; find things out. The teachers all like you. You could get away with murder.

Jeff: I'm not sure.

Jayne: It's a brilliant idea. Say you'll do it, say you'll come. It will stop all this trouble. (Pleading) Meet me there, 8 o'clock, please.

Jeff: OK, OK I will.

Jayne: Magic. *(She kisses his cheek.)* See you tonight.

(Jeff is staggered and elated. He stares after her then plays his 'Love Song'.)

Jeff's Song

Oh she'll never know quite how I love her,
Oh she'll never know quite how I care,
For her looks, for her grace, for her laughter,
For the shimmer of light in her hair,
I could stand so tall, with her there by my side
With my head held high, heart bursting with pride.

When she smiles darkness is lighter.
She can make me feel strong,
With a smile or with a gesture,
She can make right from wrong.

Oh I know that she's there with another,
And her feelings aren't really for me,
And as long as she's there with another,
Then I know that my dreams cannot be.
All I crave are looks, a smile, nothing more,
Just one caring word and my heart could soar.

For when she smiles etc.

When you're longing for someone to love you,
When you're longing for someone to care,
Then all that she does is perfection
And your heart leaps, whenever she's there.
Never mind the truth, it's dreams that become real,
For in dreams she shares the love that you feel.

And when she smiles darkness is lighter etc.

9 Tipman's house

Gran is in the chair, knitting. Jeff dashes in. He is obviously getting ready. He is putting on a sweatshirt, combing his hair, counting money, searching for the tickets, going in Mum's purse. Gran turns off the TV.

Gran: Put it down.

Jeff: What?

Gran: The purse, put it down!

Jeff: *(Realising)* It's alright, Mum knows.

Gran: Like she knew about the library tickets?

Jeff: She does, she knows. I'm going out.

Gran: Oh, are you now? Well you'd better slow down or you'll never get there.

Jeff: What?

Gran: Slow down! Stop panicking. Your blood pressure will be higher than mine.

Jeff: I've lost some tickets Gran, I need them.

Gran: They're here, I moved them. *(She holds up the tickets.)*

Jeff: Great, thanks, Gran.

                 (He goes to take them but Gran holds them back.)

Gran: What's going on Jeff?

Jeff: What do you mean?

Gran: All the panic. The other night you were miserable, no money, the other day you hated school, no mates. Now all of a sudden you can't wait to get there, you've got six tickets, a disco and people to go with.

Jeff: I'm going to be late Gran.

Gran: Who are the tickets for?

Jeff: My mates.

Gran: What mates?

Jeff: From school, lads.

Gran: And are they alright?

Jeff: Course they are.

Gran: Just 'cos you're lonely don't throw your lot in with anyone.

Jeff: Please Gran, I'll be late.

Gran: *(Still with tickets.)* Tell me about them, who are they?

Jeff: I can't tell you about them all. There's not time.

Gran: Alright, one of them, tell me about one of them.

Jeff: *(After a pause.)* There's a girl, Gran, called Jayne. She's beautiful. I think she's my girlfriend.

Gran: What do you mean, think. Don't you know?

Jeff: Not exactly, I mean I've fancied her for ages but I thought ..... you see she had this boyfriend but today she kissed me and she says she likes me. The disco was her idea. Come to the disco for me she said.

Gran: I see. Well I hope you're not disappointed.

Jeff: Disappointed? How can I be? Everything's changing. It's all working out now Gran, really it is!

Gran: I hope so love, I hope it is. Just .....

Jeff: Give me the tickets, please Gran.

Gran: Here. *(Gives him the tickets.)* Take them. Have a good time.

Jeff: *(He snatches the tickets and leaves.)* I will Gran, I will.

Gran: *(To herself.)* Just don't expect too much that's all.

10 Outside the Disco

Jeff is waiting nervously. He is seated on the wall. Behind him is a queue. All the gang except Jayne enter. Moz walks up and takes the tickets Jeff is holding. He counts them and gives them out.

Moz: Now then, shit-heap, I believe we've you to thank for our night out.

Jeff: *(Nervously)* It doesn't matter. Honest!

Moz: Oh, but we must, after all, you're our Mr Fixit now.

(Ding and Henny walk around him.)

Ding: And very smart he looks too.

Henny: Very smooth.

Ding: Got that up-market Mafia look.

Henny: Yeah, rich but ruthless.

(Janet drapes her arms over Jeff from behind, she rubs his chest and ruffles his hair, pretending to find him sexy.)

Janet: Yeah, but rugged too. God, I love powerful men. *(Obviously making fun of Jeff.)* You feel ever so strong Tipman.

Moz: Alright, be fair, Jeff's joining our little gang as junior member, so we have to be kind - now - you do want to join don't you Jeff? Jayne said you did.

Jeff: Yes, course I do.

Moz: Right then, the initiation!!

Jeff: What?

Moz: Don't worry, it's nothing serious. Stand there. Ready?

Jeff: Yeah.

Moz: Hands by your sides - that's right. Ready everyone?

(The others line up and one by one hit Jeff across the face.)

Right, you're one of us now. Happy?

Jeff: Jayne never mentioned the initiation.

Ding: She didn't know.

Henny: We never usually have one, only thought of it on the way here. *(They are beginning to laugh.)*

Janet: Look at his face. *(More laughter.)*

Ding: My, what rosy cheeks you have. *(Helpless laughter.)*

Henny: He's gob smacked. *(Laughter - laughter subsides.)*

Moz: Alright Jeff, no hard feelings. Now we're going in but you have to wait here for Jayne and give her her ticket. Think you can manage that? *(He hands Jeff two tickets.)*

Jeff: Yes course I can.

Moz: Right, we'll see you later.

               (They go into disco - all saying 'see you' etc.)

11 Jeff's daydream

All this scene takes place in Jeff's imagination.

Jeff is still seated outside the disco with the queue behind him. Enter Jayne - Jeff leaps to his feet.

Jeff: *(Surprised)* You came, you really came.

Jayne: Course I came. You can't ask a lad to a disco and not turn up can you?

Jeff: And did you?

Jayne: Did I what?

Jeff: Ask me, did you ask me?

Jayne: I'm here aren't I? I asked you didn't I? Come, come for me, that's what I said, isn't it?

Jeff: Yes, yes .....

Jayne: Well then. Did you get the tickets?

Jeff: Yes, like you said, there was no problem. *(He holds up the tickets.)*

Jayne: And Moz, and the others?

Jeff: They've gone in already.

Jayne: Are you embarrassed or something?

Jeff: No, course not, why?

Jayne: Your face, it's all red.

              (Jeff puts his hand to his face, realising and trying to look nonchalant.)

Jeff: Oh, I see. Me, embarrassed? Course not. It was just this game I was playing with Moz.

Jayne: Moz! I'd forgotten about him.

Jeff: I haven't, I can't. What's going to happen?

Jayne: What could happen?

Jeff: Well if I've got a girlfriend now.

Jayne: *(Takes his hand.)* Never mind if. You have got a girlfriend now.

Jeff: OK, now I've got a girlfriend. Now I know you like me, well that sort of puts him out of it and .....

Jayne: I phoned him before, I've explained.

Jeff: But .....

Jayne: I know too much about him, bad things, private things, all sorts. He won't make trouble for me, I can handle him. Anyway, he's fancied Janet for ages, it's all sorted out.

Jeff: All the same .....

Jayne: Look, I'll go in and make sure, you wait here till I come out again.
(She takes a ticket from his hand and exits.)

Cool Dude Rap

(The first of each pair of verses is a rap by Jeff, the (a) verses are all by backing singers in the disco queue)

1) Now stand by folks and listen to me,
Your eyes won't grasp what they can see,
It's a transformation like night from day,
Now Cool Dude's here he's on his way.

1(a) Come listen in, don't hesitate,
A change you couldn't contemplate
Has taken place this very day,
Now Cool Dude's here he's on his way.

2) Don't worry 'bout me, don't weep, don't sigh,
'Cos folks just quake when I go by.
When I'm looking at you you'd better keep still,
There'd be people dead if looks could kill.

2(a) Don't fret for him, don't weep, don't sigh,
'Cos Cool Dude's here, he's on a high.
It'll stop you dead, one glare from him,
With just one glance your lights go dim.

3) Cool Dude's the name and power's my game.
You ev'ry day folks are far too tame.
It's takin' chances that takes the biscuit,
If danger's there Cool Dude'll risk it.

3(a) Life on the edge is Cool Dude's way.
It's danger gets him through the day.
In ev'ry case he takes control,
'Cos domination's Cool Dude's goal.

4) Wit, charm, good looks and my persona
Make up a thing that others long for
That thing that draws the chicks to me
E-lec-tric Per-son-al-ity.

4(a)   The language Cool Dude speaks, you see,
        Can set a young girl's spirit free,
        When added to his ooh-la-la
        And sprinkled with Je ne sais quoi.

5)   The transformation's now complete,
        I've swept this girl right off her feet.
        The success story starts today
        'Cos Cool Dude's here he's on his way.

5(a)   Mere confidence was what he lacked.
        This girl's the key and that's a fact.
        She's altered his whole point of view.
        The story's like a dream come true.

ACT 2

SCENE 1 Outside the disco

Jeff is sitting as he was in Act 1 Scene 10. Everything is the same. Enter Jayne. This time Jeff doesn't react. We have left the dream and are back to reality.

Jayne: Hiya Jeff. *(No reply.)* Jeff, hiya. *(Still no reply, she crosses to him and prods him.)* Jeff!

Jeff: *(Very shocked, leaps up.)* God you made me jump, I was miles away. I was just thinking about you. Imagining .....

Jayne: Jeff, what are you on about?

Jeff: Oh nothing, it doesn't matter. Anyway you came, you really came.

Jayne: *(Impatient.)* Course I came. You don't ask someone to get you tickets and then not turn up do you? *(She takes a ticket from his hand.)*

Jeff: And did you?

Jayne: Did I what? It's like riddles this.

Jeff: Ask me, did you ask me?

Jayne: Who else would I ask? Get some tickets I said, for me and the gang. Get some tickets for me and I'll get you in. Hey, are you embarrassed or something?

Jeff: *(Clearly hurt.)* No, why?

Jayne: Your face, it's all red.

Jeff: *(Puts his hand to his face.)* Oh, I see. Me embarrassed? Course not, it was this game I was playing with Moz and the others.

Jayne: Moz. I'd forgotten about him.

Jeff: I hadn't.

Jayne: You're not still worried about him? I told you I've fixed it. What's wrong now?

Jeff: Nothing - anymore. I just thought, if I had a girl .....

Jayne: A girlfriend, you've got a girlfriend? I didn't even think you fancied girls. What's she like? Is she fat? How old is she? She's not a first year is she? You with a girl. I mean don't get me wrong, you're nice enough, but ..... imagine you. *(Pause)* Well, who is she? Where is she?

Jeff: You wouldn't know her. Anyway she hasn't turned up. I think I got the arrangements wrong or something.

Jayne: *(Still surprised.)* A girlfriend - I've got to tell the others. *(Turns to leave.)*

Jeff: Yeah, yeah, you go and tell them, they'd enjoy that. I'll hang on here.

Jayne: Yeah, maybe she'll come.

Jeff: No, not now, she won't come now, but I'll wait anyway.

Jayne: OK, see you after.

Jeff: Yeah.

(Jayne goes into the disco. Jeff drifts off, as he goes he kicks a drinks carton in anger and frustration.)

2 Tipman's house

The nine o'clock news is on TV. Neil is watching it. Dad enters from kitchen and passes Neil a can of beer.

Dad: Here, have a drink. *(Turns off TV.)*

Neil: Thanks Dad.

Dad: We don't get much chance to talk, you and me, do we?

Neil: No, I suppose not.

Dad: It's funny, when you were little I used to imagine the things we'd do together. *(Accepts the situation entirely.)* But things are never as you expect them, so that's that!

Neil: We did loads together. Sand castles on the beach, football, you took me to the park loads of times. That model aeroplane. And Prince. When we had Prince we took him for loads of walks.

Dad: I know but I never imagined any of that so it doesn't count. No, I meant like going to the match together, having a pint at the pub that sort of thing.

Neil: You only have to say, we can go any time. I'd like to go. It's just I get so busy I never think.

Dad: Whoa! I'm not blaming you, I didn't mean that. You've got your own life, it's not for me to interfere.

Neil: You wouldn't be interfering. I should have thought. We'll go - tomorrow - we'll go tomorrow.

Dad: Now don't go changing arrangements just because I make a few remarks.

Neil: Dad, we'll go. You're always the same you are. Apologising. It's me you're talking to, not my Mum.

Dad: Hey steady on, leave your Mum out of it. I just like a quiet life, that's all. I can't see the point of getting into battles when things usually sort themselves out anyway.

Neil: It's true though isn't it? You're always giving in to Mum.

Dad:	Not always, I can see how it seems that way but I get what I want as well, I just do it more quietly.
Neil:	She never lets you have a say. She's the same with me.
Dad:	Look if your Mum really wants something and I don't mind then what's the point of an argument? I don't want a say every time.
Neil:	And what if you do mind, what then?
Dad:	Then I pick my moment. Your Mum means well, she always does what's right in the end. Like with Gran. Your Mum wanted her in a home, she thought it was best, but Gran's here now, your Mum cares for her.
Neil:	She's always shouting at her.
Dad:	Your Mum's always shouting at everyone, it stops her having to think about things.
Neil:	Aw, come on.
Dad:	It's true. She knows your Gran's got a bad heart, she knows she's not got long, but she just carries on as normal and then she doesn't have to think about it. It's the same with you and Angela.
Neil:	I didn't even think you knew her name.
Dad:	I know a lot more than you think. I know that all your shouting won't change Mum's mind. A few quiet words are worth a month's screaming and ranting you know.
Neil:	Well what do you think? What's your opinion?
Dad:	I've told you what I think. You're a grown lad and it's not up to me to interfere in your life. And if you must know I've told your Mum that, more than once.
Neil:	It's not done much good.
Dad:	Oh you'd be surprised. She's thinking it over, she just takes time to come round to things, you mustn't expect miracles.
	(Enter Mum and Gran from front door.)
Gran:	Twenty seven, that's all I needed and I'd have had house. I'm not

going again. It's not good for me. It sends my blood pressure sky high.

Mum: Don't be daft, you know you love it. You wouldn't miss it for the world.

Gran: I'd miss getting out right enough but wouldn't miss Bingo and I wouldn't miss losing. I've never got used to that, old as I am.

Mum: Everyone loses in the end with Bingo. They're not in business to make you rich, Mother.

(Through this they have been taking off their coats. Dad rises and take the coats.)

Dad: Here, I'll take those.

Mum: Thanks love, I'll put the kettle on.

(Dad goes out with coats.)

Mum: *(To Neil)* Do you want one?

Neil: Yes, please. I'll give you a hand, I wanted a word anyway!

Mum: Alright then, you sit down Mother. *(Gran sits.)*

(Mum and Neil begin to exit during this dialogue.)

Neil: It's about Angela, I wondered whether you'd changed your mind yet.

Mum: *(As she exits to kitchen, immediately angry.)* Me? Me changed my mind!? I think you've got things a bit wrong here my lad.

(The argument continues in the kitchen. Dad enters.)

Dad: They're not at it again?

Gran: I'm afraid so.

Dad: Who started it this time?

Gran: Neil brought it up.

Dad: I told him to be patient. Why can't he listen? I'd better go and mediate I think.

(Dad leaves. Gran picks up her knitting. She is just getting started when a dejected-looking Jeff enters and flops into the chair. There is a pause.)

Gran: Everything alright?

Jeff: *(Without looking up.)* Yes. *(Pause).*

Gran: Bingo wasn't up to much tonight. *(No response.)* Same as the disco I expect. *(Pause)* I said Bingo was no good, like the disco I expect.

Jeff: I heard.

Gran: What's up - your friends not shown up?

Jeff: Course they did, they were all there.

Gran: Why didn't you stay then?

Jeff: I didn't feel well.

Gran: Oh, what's wrong? Stomach ache? Headache?

Jeff: I'm alright now.

Gran: Well, go back, catch the end, your dad will take you.

Jeff: No I don't want to.

Gran: What about your friends?

Jeff: They'll manage.

Gran: And your girlfriend?

Jeff: She's not there.

Gran: Perhaps she's not well.

Jeff: She's not my girlfriend, alright?

Gran: Well perhaps you can just be mates, friends. You know?

Jeff: Gran, forget it will you, she's not my girlfriend, I made a mistake!

(He dashes out of the room towards the hall as Mum and Dad enter from the kitchen. Mum is carrying Gran's cup of tea.)

Gran: Oh you finally got round to the cup of tea then?

Mum: I'm sorry Mum, I got a bit caught up.

Gran: I noticed.

Mum: Was that Jeff?

Gran: Yes, he's gone up to his room.

Mum: He's home early isn't he? There's nothing wrong is there?

Gran: I don't think things have gone exactly to plan.

Mum: I'll go and see him.

Dad: Doreen, don't.

Gran: I should leave him.

(Mum sinks into a chair.)

Mum: I don't know. I just don't know what to do. One storming out the back way wanting to leave home and one up in his room miserable as sin. What's wrong with this family? Can someone tell me? What's wrong? I'm sure I don't know.

Dad: I've been trying to tell you, Doreen, but you won't listen. Leave them alone, give them space, let them get on with their lives. You shouldn't get involved. You shouldn't interfere.

Mum: Somebody's got to interfere. Make sure they're doing what's right. If you don't keep your eye on them that's when the trouble starts.

Dad: Well you're not stopping trouble at the moment.

Mum: And if we did it your way, Bob Tipman, we'd just let things go. The world could be ending and you'd want to sit back and let things take their course.

Dad: Well as I see it .....

Gran: Shut up Bob.

(There is a stunned silence.)

Mum: Just a minute, Mother.

Gran: And you can shut up as well.

Mum: Mother, really!

Gran: I said shut up and I mean shut up. I might be here on sufferance but it's time I had my say before it's too late.

Mum: What do you mean too late?

Gran: Too late for everyone. You two, those boys and me. Especially me. I might not be here soon.

Dad: Now then, Evelyn, don't say that.

Gran: It's true, don't think I don't know it. I've had one heart attack, my blood pressure's up. I'm not exactly an Olympic candidate.

Mum: No but it doesn't mean .....

Gran: Doreen. Your trouble is that you think I'm stupid, you always have. Well I'm not, so shut up. Don't think I don't know what went on last year while I was ill. You went round those old folks homes didn't you? Eh?

Mum: We, we looked into it but we decided here would be best for you.

Gran: Aye, in the end when they said I might go again anytime and you felt guilty.

Dad: We only want the best, Evelyn.

Gran: That's as may be, but you never think to ask me about it. It just gets done and that's it.

Mum: *(Patronising)* Now Mother, you mustn't excite yourself.

Gran: Why not? Doesn't it fit in with your plans? I'm not thick Doreen, and I'm not incontinent either, so you can stop putting that plastic sheet on my mattress.

Dad: Evelyn, what's brought this on? We don't want any upset, that's the last thing we want. Isn't it Doreen?

Mum: Of course it is.

Gran: Well you'll listen then, because you'll be having nothing but upset if you don't change your way with those two boys. I've sat back for long enough. I've got to have my say now. You're both as bad as each other. You Doreen, you want to run their lives. Make them live your way. All the time you're twisting them, pushing them in your direction. With Neil it's his girlfriend. With Jeff you tell him not to worry and send him to school but you never face the issues. You never ask them how they feel or what they need.

Dad: *(Self righteously)* I've said this myself Evelyn.

Gran: Well there's no need to be so smug because you're just as bad. Sometimes you can't just sit back. That's what Neil keeps saying. Sometimes you've got to go for what you want. And Jeff, he comes to you when he's unhappy, frightened at school and what do you tell him - don't worry it's part of growing up.

Dad: Well it is.

Gran: Is it? Where does it say that? Where does it say growing up has to involve pain? Where does it say you have to get your eyes blacked and your fingers broken before you're an adult? And you Doreen, where does it say you're only allowed to love who your mother loves? Or that mothers can blackmail their children with threats of homelessness and constant arguments?

Mum: I don't remember you exactly welcoming Bob with open arms Mother.

Gran: That's right, I didn't but I was wrong and I said so. I said so then and I'm saying so now. So do you want to make the same mistake just because I did? You don't have to be my age before you learn common sense. It can happen beforehand you know.

Mum: We're not trying to hurt them Mother, it's just that we love them.

Dad: Aye, we've always had their best interests at heart. I mean, what more can we do?

Gran: Tell them. Tell them you love them. It's not pain people learn from, it's love. So tell them you love them then stand back and trust them. They need your support. If they know you're with them they'll make the right decisions. You might not always agree, but that's not the point. It's what's best for them that counts and with your support they'll find it. Why do you think Neil fights so hard? Because when he's with Angela he feels loved. He believes in himself. And why do you think Jeff's so unhappy. He needs you to give him strength. Help him believe in himself. *(There is a long pause.)* Well, I'm off to my bed. There's no more left to say and I'm not so sure you'd listen in any event. Good night. *(Gran exits.)*

Mum: Good night Mother.

Dad: Good night Evelyn.

3 The school yard

It is Monday and pupils are arriving at school. The gang are discussing Jeff and the disco.

Ding: That's what I'm saying, he must have just cleared off.

Henny: I know that but why? What's he up to?

Ding: How should I know?

Janet: Perhaps he didn't feel well.

Ding: Don't be stupid.

Janet: He might have had tummy ache, poor boy! *(Giggles)*

Henny: You don't just get a load of disco tickets and then not show up. It's not normal.

Ding: That's true, I mean we did invite him didn't we?

Henny: I suppose we did, sort of.

Ding: Perhaps he's still scared.

Henny: Perhaps he's just boring like he always was.

Janet: *(Giggling)* I know, perhaps he wet himself while he was talking to Jayne. He fancies you, you know.

Jayne: Get lost - does he heck. *(She's embarrassed.)*

Janet: Course he does, he's always staring at you in History and in Maths.

Jayne: *(Aware of Moz.)* Get lost, Janet. *(Firmly)* Shut it. Anyway he said he was waiting for a girl.

Moz: *(Ignoring all the banter.)* Alright, you saw him last, what was he like? Is he setting us up with these tickets or what?

Jayne: No he wouldn't do that. He had one himself. It was in his hand. Anyway if he was setting us up they'd have got us on Friday, at the disco. Myers wouldn't have missed a chance like that.

Henny: If he was waiting for a girl, why did he only have one ticket in his hand?

Ding: Sherlock Holmes! Daa-Daah. *(Like 'who dunnit' music.)*

Janet: So it was you. There was no other girl. It was you.

                (Janet is now winding Jayne up and making more sense than she realises. Moz is becoming annoyed and Jayne is desperate to change the subject.)

Janet: Did you kiss him Jayne? Was he passionate? Does his breath smell?

Jayne: *(Angry)* Shut your mouth, he said he was waiting for another girl. He might have had two tickets, how do I know?

Ding: I bet it was a first year and he didn't want to tell us.

Henny: Can you imagine being stood up by a first year? What an idiot.

Moz: Right, shut up. Jayne's right, he wouldn't set us up with the tickets, he's not brave enough. But he did clear off and that's out of order, I gave him a chance.

Henny: Yeah it was rude, let's smack him round, teach him.

Janet: He did get us the tickets.

Ding: So what, let's smack him round anyway. *(They laugh.)*

Jayne: Moz we agreed. It's gone too far with him. We said we should ease off. We can't go on hurting him. Myers will have us, he's really after you.

Janet: It's true, see. Her and Tipman have got a thing going.

Moz: Shut up, Janet, you're being stupid.

Jayne: I mean he only had my word I could fix things. Perhaps he wasn't sure.

Ding: Course he was sure - we initiated him. *(They all laugh.)*

Jayne: That's what I mean bonehead. I tell him he's in the gang then you lot go and batter him. What's he supposed to think? Moz, you should talk to him. Tell him he's in and no battering this time.

Henny: He'd look soft, sucking up to Tipman. I still say we should smack him a bit.

Moz: No, Henny, she's right. We get him in and we stitch him up. Ding, go and find him. *(Ding goes.)* I mean if he's just a nobody in the gang then nothing's changed. So we have to find someone he's in charge of, give him a bit of power.

Henny: That new kid, Richardson, the one we put in the brook, he'll do. Tipman can smack him about. I still can't see why though.

Moz: Nobody gets smacked about. We just screw Richardson for a few bob but Tipman takes the money. That way he's in with us. He's done it. He'll say nothing about the disco tickets and he'll say nothing to Myers 'cos if he does he cops it 'cos of Richardson.

Henny: Perfect, like insurance. He's in the gang but he's still in our power.

Jayne: Here's Ding - he's got Tipman. *(Ding and Jeff approach. Ding is apparently reassuring Jeff. Jeff looks apprehensive.)*

Ding: Honest, he's not after you. We were worried on Friday.

Moz: *(Ostentatiously friendly.)* Jeff! We were worried! What happened on Friday?

Jeff: *(Still apprehensive.)* Friday?

Moz: Yes, at the disco.

Jeff: Oh, then?

Moz: Yeah, we missed you mate. Thought you were coming in, then you disappeared. Weren't you well?

Jeff: *(Accepting the excuse.)* No, that's right, I felt a bit off so I went home.

Janet: Jayne said you had a girlfriend. *(Jeff looks at Jayne with embarrassment.)*

Jeff: No, no girlfriend, I was joking, I just didn't feel well.

Moz: But you're OK now?

Jeff: Yeah!

Moz: Great. Now, listen. At break we're going to need you.

Jeff: Me?

Henny: Yeah you, we're expanding operations. *(Jeff looks puzzled.)*

Moz: You are in the gang now, aren't you Jeff?

Jeff: Course, course I am.

Moz: Right. At break you find Richardson. Know him? That geek who's always crying. *(Jeff nods.)* Right well bring him here at break, after Myers' lesson. He's going to make a contribution to our social fund.

                (Bell rings. Enter Mr Kershaw.)

Mr Kershaw: C'mon you lot, get moving. Get to registration.

Moz: *(To Jeff)* Don't forget.

Jeff: I won't.

Mr Kershaw: Morris, Tipman, you dogs. Get moving.

4 Myers' lesson

The class are seated as in Act 1 and Mr Myers is delivering a History lesson.

Mr Myers: And right in the middle of East Germany remained Berlin, but split into two, East and West.

David: Well if it was all sorted out, why did they change it all again?

Mr Myers: That's the point David, it wasn't sorted out, at least not as far as the people were concerned.

Sandra: But we don't go on fighting over borders in this country Sir, we don't argue, not like them.

Mr Myers: I shouldn't tell the Welsh that, or the Scots.

Jayne: Or the Irish.

Mr Myers: Exactly Jayne. You see the thing is, when the map of Europe was drawn again, after World War 2, it was drawn for the winners, not the losers.

Caroline: Well what about Poland or Yugoslavia and all them Sir?

Mr Myers: Basically, they didn't matter. What mattered for Britain, America and Russia was that they got the best settlement for themselves. They wanted to preserve their power. So they set up borders that suited them. Often, these borders had nothing to do with history or even nationality, they were merely convenient in a political sense.

Jayne: But what about all the people who lived there?

Mr Myers: They had no power, so they had no say. Simple. World politics in a nutshell.

Mark: But whose idea was it? Who thought of doing it?

Mr Myers: I suppose the answer to that is nobody really.

Mark: But someone must have. I mean when the war ended someone must have suggested it.

Mr Myers: But that's the point, no-one needed to. It's been going on for years. Since the days of the Roman Empire and even before that. Just this century, after the Revolution, Russia seized huge tracts of land from other countries. In the 1920's Britain and France re-drew the map of the Middle East so they could control oil production. And even now, America and others like them expand their wealth and power by interfering in the affairs of weaker and poorer countries. The idea's not new Mark, the strong have always stolen from the weak.

David: So all these wars, Sir, like in Europe or in the Middle East are really people fighting to get their countries back.

Mr Myers: Partly, David, at least, and usually they try to steal a bit more whilst they're about it.

Sandra: But why does it happen all of a sudden? Why all at once? Saddam Hussein, Communism collapsing, Yugoslavia fighting.

Mr Myers: It doesn't, it just seems that way. If you take things by force eventually the balance will change. People resent it and resentment doesn't go away. It may take years but the balance of power always changes. For all sorts of reasons. Maybe the government goes too far, maybe the people are so poor they have nothing left to lose. It doesn't really matter why, but one day the victim bites back and the turmoil starts all over again.

Caroline: But Sir, what if .....

Mr Myers: What if, Caroline, I exercise *my* power. You've had me talking for long enough. So the map you haven't drawn and the notes on border changes can be done for homework. *(Groans)*

                (The bell rings.)

Caroline: One day Sir we might bite back.

Mr Myers: Yes, but not now Caroline, because the bell's gone and it's break. Off you go.

                (Class begins to disperse. Mr Myers looks towards Jeff.)

Mr Myers: Jeff, a minute please.

Jeff: Yes Sir?

Mr Myers: Morris. I saw you with him this morning from the staffroom window. And Friday, at the disco.

Jeff:	*(Questioning)* Yes Sir?
Mr Myers:	He's picking on you isn't he?
Jeff:	No Sir, no, we're mates, really.
Mr Myers:	If you tell me Jeff I can do something.
Jeff:	There's no problem Sir, honest.
Mr Myers:	When do you start work experience?
Jeff:	Monday Sir, everyone does.
Mr Myers:	Where are you going?
Jeff:	Thorneycrofts Sir. They're solicitors in town.
Mr Myers:	Jeff you've got two weeks away from Morris and all of them. Think about it while you're at Thorneycrofts. Tell me what's going on and I can stop it permanently. No more Morris, no more misery.
Jeff:	But Sir, I'm fine. They're my mates, really!
Mr Myers:	*(Resignedly)* Enjoy work experience Jeff
	(Jeff exits and Mr Myers packs up books, etc.)

5   The school yard

Morning break. There is the normal hustle and bustle of the school yard as in previous scenes. Jeff enters and is pounced upon by Moz.

Moz:	You took your time didn't you? What did Myers want?
Jeff:	Work experience, he was asking about work experience.
Moz:	Are you sure?
Jeff:	Course I am. What's wrong? Why is it important?
Moz:	It's not, it doesn't matter, forget it.

Jeff: I can't find Richardson. I can't find him anywhere.

Moz: Well we saved you a job, we got him for you.

                    (Ding and Henny emerge from the crowd with a small and obviously terrified Richardson - they are roughing him up.)

Jeff: So is that it - then? Do we let him go now?

Moz: We do not! Our friend Richardson is going to give us some money, aren't you Richardson?

Richardson: *(Pleading)* I haven't got any Moz, honest I haven't.

                    (Ding and Henny twist his arms, Richardson screams.)

Moz: Search him Jeff. *(Jeff hesitates.)* Go on search him.

                    (Jeff searches him and finds money.)

Moz: So you were lying Richardson.

Richardson: It's my dinner money, please Moz and my bus fare, it's all I've got, I'll be starving, I'll have to walk home.

                    (Ding and Henny laugh, Moz turns his back. Jeff holds out the money to Moz.)

Moz: Keep it, it's yours. *(Jeff hesitates.)* Go on, put it in your pocket. *(Jeff does.)* Right! Good! Now hit Richardson.

Jeff: *(Astonished)* What?

Moz: Hit him for lying. *(Jeff half heartedly hits Richardson).*

Moz: *(With menace)* Properly Tipman. Do it properly. *(Jeff hits Richardson hard to the stomach. He is surprised by the reaction but excited and immediately hits again but harder. Richardson is clearly hurt.)*

Moz: Whoa, whoa, don't go too far. *(He restrains Jeff.)* You are keen Jeffrey, aren't you? *(Turns to Richardson.)* And remember, worm, keep your mouth shut or you'll really get done. *(To Ding and Henny.)* Let him go. *(Ding and Henny release him, kicking him up the backside as he goes.)*

Moz: Well now Jeff, you did well, you're really one of us now.

6 Tipman's house

A few days have passed. Jeff is now on Work Experience. The television news is on. Gran is knitting. Gran rises muttering about the news and turns off the TV.

Gran: The state of them fighting, bombing and all the rest of it. Is it any wonder families have arguments?

Gran's Song

They think I'm old and crotchety.
They think I'm right off my head.
And though they all say otherwise
They'd sooner I was dead.
And though my vigour has all been lost
My mind is just as it was.

Chorus   I think of the times when I was a lover,
I think of the times when I wasn't just old,
I think about times when I could be a mother,
Of the times I was a person too,
Of the times I was a person too.

I'm sent to bingo twice a week,
Well that's what you do with the old.
They took my home, my memories,
Insisted they were sold.
I've lost my pride, my dignity,
I've lost the right to be free.

Chorus   Seems that the girl that I raised to a woman is raising me,
Taking my rights, I'm not asked, I'm simply told.
Seems that the world that I worked for is cheating me
Of the time I was a person too,
Of the time I could be a person too.

(Gran settles back into her chair. Enter Jeff. He is carrying a folder/document case and is clearly dressed for the office.)

Gran: Hello love, I didn't realise it was that time.

Jeff: *(Kissing her.)* Hiya Gran.

Gran: My word don't you look wonderful, so grown up.

Jeff: *(Embarrassed)* Gra-a-an.

Gran: You do though, you look marvellous. And happy too. You're enjoying it at Thorneycroft's aren't you?

Jeff: It's alright, yeah.

Gran: Do you fancy being a solicitor?

Jeff: I do really, it would be good.

Gran: I can see you now, the last minute of a vital case and suddenly you come up with the missing witness.

Jeff: That's Perry Mason, Gran, not real life. Real life is mostly buying houses and arguing who gets the garden shed in a divorce case.

Gran: Well I can dream. All the same, you are happy?

Jeff: *(Pleased she's asked.)* Yes, Gran, I am.

Gran: Well it's a bit of a contrast to school then isn't it?

Jeff: Yes.

Gran: What goes on there Jeff? Tell me please. *(Jeff is silent).* They pick on you don't they? *(Pause)* Those broken fingers last term, they weren't from climbing trees were they? *(Pause)* And the black eyes and the bruises. They didn't come from playing football, you hate football. Tell me, Jeff, please. Tell me what's going on.

Jeff: I'm just unhappy sometimes.

Gran: You don't have to tell me that, it stands out a mile. *(Long pause)* Jeff, please.

Jeff: *(Quietly)* I'm frightened.

Gran: Pardon?

Jeff: *(Louder)* I'm frightened. I'm frightened to do things on my own, I'm frightened of other people, I'm even frightened of losing you!

Gran: Well you mustn't worry about me. You will lose me. But don't be scared. I'm not. It was always going to happen. I don't know when, but I'm fairly sure how. My heart will go and that will be it.

Jeff: How can you just say that Gran?

Gran: Because it's true. I can't change it so I'll face it. I'm happy with my life - I've missed nothing, I regret nothing. I've done my best so now I'll face the music. You should do the same.

Jeff: It's not a case of doing my best, I already do. I pass exams, I do my homework. I'm frightened. I've just told you. I thought you'd understand.

Gran: I'm trying, Jeff, but you've told me nothing really. You're so close these days. Remember, when we always used to be joking, all the fun we had?

Jeff: That's gone Gran. I was a kid then, things were simple.

Gran: Stuff and nonsense. It was twelve months ago. Anyway things are never simple, they just seem that way when you look back. You must tell me what it is you're so frightened of. Please Jeff, let me help, *(long pause)* please.

Jeff: It's these lads and girls at school, they pick on me, hurt me, sometimes they take my money.

Gran: Then you should have told somebody and have them stop it.

Jeff: *(Panic)* I can't, you can't, they'll just get me again. Promise Gran, promise you'll say nothing. If you do I'll just say it's all a lie, you can't make me tell, I'll say you've got it wrong.

Gran: Calm down, I'll say nothing, I don't know so very much.

Jeff: Why me? That's what I can't understand. Why me? What's wrong with me that I attract them? Why not somebody else?

Gran: There's nothing wrong with you, ignore them, mix with other people.

Jeff: I can't because they follow me. Other people don't want to be involved in case they're next on the list so I'm left on my own, isolated. Sometimes I'm even glad when they come over. At least someone is noticing me.

Gran: Oh Jeff, you're worth more than that. We must do something, change things.

Jeff: No need Gran, it's OK now. I've made friends with them.

Gran: Friends? How can you have friends who cause you so much grief?

Jeff: But it's safer, don't you see? They still pick on me a bit, take the mickey but they don't hurt me, so it's better now.

Gran: *(Scornful)* Well that's a backwards way of viewing things. You don't like them, you're frightened of them, so you join in with them and put up with their bullying because it feels safer.

Jeff: Not feels safer, Gran, it is safer.

Gran: But what price do you pay? *(Jeff looks puzzled.)* I'll tell you, you're the price, you stop being you. You turn yourself over to them and you stop being important.

Jeff: What else can I do? I've told you, they bully me, they pick on me, they hurt me. It's alright for you.

Gran: Is it? Do you think I've never been picked on. It's still happening now. Plastic sheets on the mattress, brochures for Sunnyside homes on the coffee table. It's no different. They just think it is because they pretend it's in my best interests.

Jeff: But it is different, don't you see, you're not frightened and I am.

Gran: Well don't let them see it. Learn the lesson I learned many years ago. The real cowards are the bullies. You're their only strength. It's only through you that they feel tough. You don't need them. If they went tomorrow you'd not care in the slightest, but if you went they'd be nothing. They need you, you're the person that helps them love themselves. Without a victim they're nothing.

Jeff: But they hurt me Gran. *(Exasperated)* I'm frightened.

Gran: Physically, they only hurt you physically. But if you make them your friends they take your mind, they take everything. Be Jeff Tipman, be yourself, then every time they hurt you you can laugh because they're the weak ones and they say so with every act of violence.

Jeff: Well that's great. Just like 'The Sound of Music'. Next time I'm spitting blood I'll whistle a happy tune.

Gran: *(Angry)* You know what I mean. Don't let them rule you, don't let them change you. No matter how tough they seem they're pathetic. Don't get sucked into their world, Jeff, turn them in.

Jeff:	I can't Gran, I can't and you mustn't either.
Gran:	Oh I won't, don't you worry. It's something you must do.
Jeff:	I can't Gran, I haven't the courage. I can't do it on my own.
Gran:	The courage is there, Jeff, it will come and you won't be on your own. You take that step and you'll be surprised how many others will come and join you. You're back at school on Monday. Turn them in, put a stop to it.
Jeff:	I can't Gran, I can't.
Gran:	Well, we'll see and I'll be watching. Don't let me down Jeff. I need you. I need to know I've left good things behind me.

7 The school yard

Work experience is over. Moz, Ding, Henny, Janet, Jayne and Jeff are all picking on Richardson. Richardson is surrounded and during the dialogue the gang members close in on him. There are a number of onlookers in the background.

Richardson:	Come on Moz, let me off. You can have all next week's dinner money - Tipman tell them, it's five quid, more if you count my spends. Please.
Ding:	It's not your money we want.
Henny:	But we'll have it anyway.
Moz:	No, it's not just a question of money. Two weeks you've had without us. Two weeks and we've not expected a penny have we Tippo?
Jeff:	No, Moz.
Ding:	Which was a bit generous really, Richardson, wasn't it?
Richardson:	*(Frightened)* Yes.
Henny:	So why have you put it round that your brother beat up Moz?
Richardson:	I didn't, I haven't even got a brother.

Moz: McMahon says you did.

Richardson: Please Moz, he's a liar.

Ding: Lots of people believe him.

Henny: And rumours can be very upsetting.

Moz: So you're going to tell everyone I'm the boss and you're a liar.

Richardson: I will, I will, I'll tell them. *(Shouts)* Moz's the boss and I'm a liar.

Moz: Good! Now take your trousers down. Tell them you're a queer.

Richardson: Please Moz, not that please.

Janet: Smack him, Moz, go on smack him.

Moz: Take your pants down. Tell them you fancy Tipman.

Richardson: Please, Moz. Please.

Moz: *(Menacing)* Do it! *(Richardson lets his trousers fall.)*

Richardson: I'm queer, I'm queer. I fancy Jeff Tipman.

Moz: Louder!

Richardson: *(Crying)* I'm queer. I fancy Jeff Tipman.

Janet: Now smack him Moz. *(Richardson, degraded, pulls up his trousers. The gang have closed in. Moz grabs Richardson.)*

Moz: You see Richardson people must know I'm in charge, stories like that damage me.

Richardson: *(In pain from Moz's grip.)* It was a joke, honest. I'm sorry. I'll do anything. Please Moz.

Jayne: Moz don't hurt him. Please Moz. No more.

Moz: You got any pets Richardson?

Richardson: You know I have, I've got a rabbit.

Moz: What's it called, Richardson?

Richardson:	*(Very quietly)* Bo Bo.
Moz:	*(Twists his arm.)* Louder!
Richardson:	Bo Bo, Moz, it's called Bo Bo. *(The others laugh.)*
Moz:	Nice name, Bo Bo isn't it? Isn't it?
Richardson:	Yeah.
Moz:	*(Harshly)* Kill it.
Richardson:	What?
Moz:	Kill it. Kill it tonight and bring it in tomorrow.
Richardson:	Please Moz, I can't, I've had him for years. I love him. Please Moz I can't kill him.
Moz:	Kill it or you get really pasted. *(He throws Richardson to the ground - the boy is crying.)* Sort him out Tipman, put the boot in. He called you a queer.
Gran's Voice:	*(Echoing in Jeff's conscience)* Jeff. The price is you!
Moz:	Come on Tipman do it.
Jayne:	Moz, don't make him.
All:	Do it, Tipman.
Gran's Voice:	The price is you. The price is you.
	(Jeff appears to be about to kick Richardson when Neil, who has entered unseen, calls out.)
Neil:	Jeff. *(The gang and the others scatter.)*
Jeff:	Neil.
Neil:	What's going on? *(Neil and Jeff are now alone.)*
Jeff:	Nothing's going on, what do you mean?
Neil:	The crowd, the noise - were they picking on you again?

Jeff: *(Dismissive) No. (Thinking on his feet.)* It was this game you see, it was a game and .....

Neil: OK never mind listen, you've .....

Jeff: *(Seeing car keys in Neil's hand)* Hey, you've got the car. How come Dad let you have the car.? He never usually .....

Neil: Jeff! Shut up, listen. I've got the car because Gran's ill. Mum and Dad have gone in the ambulance. I've come for you. *(There is a brief pause, they stare at each other.)*

8 Tipman's house

Everyone is dressed up, but in sombre funeral clothes. The table has paper plates, cups, saucers, etc. strewn on it. Neil and Jeff are putting rubbish in a bin sack. Mum is just finishing a cup of tea seated in 'Gran's' chair. Dad enters from hall, he has been seeing off the guests.

Dad: Well that's the last. *(With forced cheer.)* I don't know, it always seems to be George. Wherever he goes he's always the last. Ah well, no harm done. Let's get this lot cleared away. *(He crosses and begins to pile cups, etc onto a tray.)*

Mum: *(Very firmly)* Leave them.

Dad: Eh?

Mum: Leave them.

Neil: It won't take a minute Mum and then .....

Mum: I've something to say, leave them for now. *(The others stop and look at Mum.)* It won't take long but I've been thinking. Gran's dead, the funeral's over and here we are collecting plates. People always find things to clear up after funerals, but they're always physical things, never emotional things. Gran worried me, she said it's going to be too late. Well it's not, it's not going to be too late. *(Brief pause as she gathers herself.)* Neil, I've put out some stuff in Gran's room, have a look. If you want it, take it and anything else in there for that matter.

Neil: Mum .....

Mum:	*(Won't be interrupted.)* Shsh. If you want to set up with Angela, and you're sure, then that's up to you, not me. Do it with my blessing. You and Angela will always be welcome here, won't they Bob?
Bob:	Aye, of course, always. *(He is clearly bemused.)*
Mum:	And you Jeff, Gran spoke to me about you.
Jeff:	*(Alarmed)* What did she say?
Mum:	I'm not really sure. Just that you were going to need me, need all of us.
Jeff:	*(Uncomfortable)* I don't know what she means. *(Realises his mistake.)* What she meant.
Mum:	Well that doesn't matter, I just want you to know that we support you, me and your Dad. We love you very much and never want to see you hurt. No matter what happens you can count on us.
Jeff:	What if it was something bad? What if I'd hurt someone or stolen something?
Mum:	No matter what I'd try to understand and see your side. You don't have to be ashamed with me, I'm your Mum. If there's something you've done, something you fear, I'll be there, and your Dad will. *(There's a pause.)* Now don't stand here gawping, all of you. I thought we were cleaning up in here.

9 The school yard

Morning. Moz, Ding, Henny, Jayne, Janet are all together. Richardson runs in.

Richardson:	Moz, Moz. *(Pushing through the others.)*
Moz:	What do you want, worm?
Richardson:	Tipman's back, Tipman's back.
Moz:	So?
Richardson:	I thought you'd want to know.

Moz: Why would we want to know? *(Others laugh.)*

Richardson: Well he's one of the gang.

Henny: When we let him. *(General laughter.)*

Janet: Is that it, then, Richardson? Is that all you wanted?

Ding: Or did you want to kiss my feet again?

Richardson: I've got an idea, for winding up Tipman.

Moz: Oh aye?

Richardson: The funeral march.

Henny: Eh?

Richardson: The funeral march. His Gran's just died, last week. When he comes in we'll sing the funeral march.

Ding: *(Laughing)* He'll go spare.

Janet: I bet he cries when we sing it, I bet he cries.

Jayne: You can't Moz, you can't do that.

Moz: Shut up Jayne, don't be boring. It's good that Ricko, I like it. Go and get him. *(Richardson goes.)*

Jayne: You can't do it Moz. It's really tight.

Janet: Shut up, Jayne, it will be a laugh.

Moz: Don't start till I tell you. Shut up now, he's here. *(Enter Jeff and Richardson.)*

Moz: Hiya Jeff.

Jeff: Moz.

Moz: Ricko found you then?

Jeff: Yeah.

Moz: Been a big mate while you've been missing has little Ricko.

                (To others.) Hasn't he? *(General agreement.)* A week's a long time to be gone. We were even thinking of promoting little Ricko above you. *(General agreement.)* Still you're back now, welcome back. *(He waves his hands to urge on the others who echo welcome back, welcome back.)* Little Ricko, missed you, didn't you Ricko?

Richardson: Yeah, Moz.

Moz: So he invented a game for you. Do you want to play Tippo?

Jeff: *(Not really interested.)* If you want.

Moz: Now don't be like that. It's good, it's like Name That Tune. We sing, you listen, then you guess the title. Ready everyone?

Jayne: Moz.

Moz: After three - three. *(The gang begin to sing the funeral march. Jeff turns away.)*

Janet: Is he crying? *(Others continue singing.)*

Moz: Guessed it yet, Tippo?

    (Jeff turns.)

Jeff: Leave my Gran out of it.

Moz: No ideas?

Jeff: Make them stop, Moz.

Jayne: Moz, please.

Moz: Have a guess, go on.

Jeff: Stop them.

Moz: Or? *(The singing goes quieter. Moz holds Jeff's face between finger and thumb.)* What will you do? *(The atmosphere has become very threatening. Richardson is looking on closely - the crowd have closed in.)*

Richardson: *(Very softly)* Hit him, Moz, hit him.

Moz: Well, shit heap? What will you do?

Jayne: Did they sing it when your Mum died? *(Moz immediately stiffens and turns.)*

Moz: What did you say? What did you say?

Jayne: When your Mum died did you play Name That Tune?

                  (Moz leaps across to Jayne and hits her across the face and then grabs her by the hair.)

Moz: You bitch!

Jeff: *(He starts forward.)* Jayne.

Jayne: You going to beat me up now?

Jeff: Get off her.

Ding: Moz.

Henny: Leave her mate.

Janet: It's him. *(Pointing to Richardson.)* It was his idea. It's his fault. *(Moz releases Jayne, he is clearly insane with temper.)*

Moz: That's right. You thought of it Richardson.

Richardson: Please, Moz, no. It was a joke, a joke. *(Moz begins to beat and kick Richardson cursing him, blaming him. Richardson pleads, the others are shouting. Jeff propels himself forward and barges Moz away from Richardson.)*

Moz: *(Turns and sees Jeff.)* You bastard. *(He seizes Jeff and punctuates his next line by punching him.)* Never - never - touch me again - or you are dead. *(Throws him to the ground.)*

10 The school yard

Immediately afterwards. Jeff and Richardson are sitting side by side. They are licking their wounds.

Richardson: You're mad, he'll have you.

Jeff: What's new? He'll have me anyway.

Richardson:	He wasn't really hurting me.
Jeff:	I noticed.
Richardson:	He just flipped, though, did you see? What set him off?
Jeff:	Dunno. He doesn't need anything. He's just crazy.
Richardson:	He's alright, you just have to be careful.
Jeff:	Oh, that sounds fair. Moz is basically reasonable. Did you tell your rabbit that?
Richardson:	What?
Jeff:	Your rabbit, when you killed it.
Richardson:	I didn't. I couldn't.
Jeff:	So what happened?
Richardson:	I got a pasting like he said. They beat me up, and then when I got home the rabbit was gone. They'd been and taken it.
Jeff:	Well somebody's got to stop him. I've had enough.
Richardson:	What will you do?
Jeff:	I'm telling Myers. I'm telling Myers everything.
Richardson:	You can't grass, Moz will kill you. You've seen him, he'll go berserk.
Jeff:	He can do what he likes and anyway, it's not grassing - it's telling the truth for a change. *(He stands and begins to leave.)*
Richardson:	*(Standing, calls after Jeff.)* And what about me? What will I do? I'm not talking, I won't say anything.
Jeff:	OK.
Richardson:	I'll tell him, I'll tell Moz. He'll have you.
Jeff:	Tell him what you like. Tell him I'll be waiting. *(Turns and exits.)*
	(Richardson looks after him, then turns to exit shouting.)
Richardson:	Moz, Moz.

11 The school yard

The beginning of lunchtime. Moz and the rest are in a huddle with Richardson. Jayne is absent. From a distance comes the voice of Mr Myers.

Mr Myers: Morris, Morris.

                  (The group spread out. Moz is left centre stage as Mr Myers, followed by Mr Kershaw enters.)

Mr Myers: I want you Morris and so does the Head.

Moz: Yes Sir? What for Sir?

Mr Myers: You know very well what for and this time I've got all I need to prove it.

Moz: Prove what Sir?

Mr Myers: Don't try to be clever, just get along to the Head.

Moz: If you're talking about Tipman, Sir, he's always making up stories. Everyone knows it. *(General assent.)* I don't think he likes me. *(Sniggers)* I mean it's his word against mine and I've got loads of witnesses. And anyway he's ugly.

Mr Myers: *(Eyeball to eyeball.)* And how beautiful are you Morris? How beautiful are you? *(Pause as they stare at each other.)* Get to the Head.

Mr Kershaw: Yes go on Morris, you ape. Get to the Head. You're disgusting. You're thick, lad. You're an animal. You're nothing but a piece of slime.

Moz: *(Turns to leave, then under his breath.)* Piss off Kershaw. *(To the others.)* Back in a bit.

Mr Kershaw: *(To Mr Myers.)* Did you hear that? I heard that Morris. I'll have you lad, I'll paste the walls with you. *(To Mr Myers.)* Little upstart. They've no manners, any of them. I shall have him!

Mr Myers: Yes Mr Kershaw.

12 The school yard

Towards the end of lunchtime. The gang regroup. Jayne is now with them.

Henny: If they've got him then they've got us, we're in for it as well.

Ding: Moz won't grass.

Janet: I never hit anyone. I never had the money.

Jayne: And you never stopped anyone, so shut it.

Janet: Listen to Miss Prissy Knickers. I never heard you protesting.

Henny: Just shut up, keep your mouths shut and they can't do anything. *(Moz enters furtively, the gang greet him with a barrage of questions.)*

All: What's gone on?

Moz?

What happened?

What did he say?

Moz: I've been sent home.

Ding: When?

Moz: Now, straight away. They reckon Tipman's told them everything.

Henny: What about us?

Moz: Never mentioned you and I've said nothing.

Ding: If he's talked though, we've all had it.

Moz: They're bluffing. If Tipman had really told them they'd have sent for you. He's too frightened, he's said nothing.

Janet: Ask him. *(She indicates Jeff and the gang look up.)*

Moz: I want you Tipman.

Jeff: I thought you might, Morris. *(Murmur of surprise at this brave reply)*

Moz: People tell me you've been talking.

Jeff: People would be right.

Moz: I'm going to kill you, Tipman. I'm going to kick your head in.

Jeff: But you can't, can you? Not right now. Haven't you got to go home or something?

Moz: *(Advances on Jeff and grips his face in usual finger and thumb manner.)* But I'll be back. Three thirty and I'll be back, up by the shops and you're getting what's coming. Scared Tipman?

Jeff: *(Unmoved)* Not really, not now.

Moz: Well you're going to be, because there's no escape. There's nowhere for you to run.

Jeff: I wouldn't dream of it. I'll be there. I wouldn't miss it for the world.

Moz: What are you up to? What are you trying to pull?

Jeff: Nothing Moz, nothing at all. I'm just not scared any more. Find that confusing do you?

Moz: I know what I do find ..... *(He shapes up to hit Jeff.)*

Jayne: *(Grips his arm.)* Moz, enough. It's gone too far.

Moz: Oh aye? You turning chicken?

Jayne: Call it what you want but I've had enough.

Moz: *(Lowers his hand.)* Janet was right about you two. You've got the hots for him. Well try kissing that, lover girl. *(He spits in Jeff's face.)* C'mon you lot. 3.30 Tipman.

              (They exit leaving Jayne and Jeff on stage. Jayne crosses and wipes his face.)

Jeff: It was you, you know, at the disco. You were the girl I was waiting for.

Jayne: I know. I didn't then, but I do now. I'm a bit thick with lads.

Jeff: I noticed.

Jayne: I don't fancy you, you know. I stuck up for you but I don't fancy you.

Jeff: I'd noticed that as well.

Jayne: Sorry.

Jeff: It's OK.

Jayne: It doesn't work, you see, two people, one madly in love and the other not caring. It wouldn't work for you and it didn't work for me and Moz.

Jeff: I know, it doesn't matter, not now. It was just a day dream.

Jayne: Don't go, Jeff. Don't go at 3.30. He'll be there, you know. So will Ding and Henny.

Jeff: I know.

Jayne: Well, go home now, don't wait. He's mad, he'll really hurt you.

Jeff: Oh, he's done that, he's done that loads of times. But this time I'm going to finish it once and for all.

(Jeff exits, Jayne stares after him.)

Jayne's Song

Gone now, he's gone now, but yet it's not hurting me.
Now that it's over I feel finally free.
He never bought any flowers, he never once said he was mine.
His tenderness was all secret, but somehow that always seemed fine.

Chorus   I'd have done anything just to make him think fondly about me.
I'd have done anything but the love in our lives all came from me.

I thought that loving meant me ceasing to exist.
I was his servant the moment that we first kissed.
I gave up all of my freedom, I sacrificed most of my friends.
I followed wherever he led me but none of it helped in the end.

Chorus

Now as I look back, I see just where it went wrong.
Love must be equal or love can never be strong.
I gave my heart without question, my feelings were never returned.
I offered my understanding but all of my gestures were spurned.

Chorus

Wounded, but wiser, I'll do what's right and act with pride.
I'll cry in private and keep my anguish inside.
I'll tell of his hatred and ego, I'll tell of his cowardice too.
Make no mistake it's not courage, that led him to hurt those he
knew.

Chorus

13 Tipman's house

Mum is pottering about dusting, etc. She hears a noise.

Mum:	Is that you Neil?

Neil:	Yes.

Mum:	You forgot that duvet last night. It's in your Gran's room. Sorry, the guest room, I must get into the habit.

Neil:	Mum, where's Jeff?

Mum:	At school, he went back today, what's wrong?

Neil:	I don't know. This girl saw me on the path and shouted. She said Jeff was in trouble, real trouble then ran away. She was crying.

Mum:	*(Agitated)* Who was she, what did she look like?

Neil:	I don't know, dark haired, she just said tell his Mum and ran off down the hill.

Mum:	*(Businesslike, removing her apron.)* Get your Dad. He's up the road at Arthur's, get him and get up to that school. I'll see you there.

14 Outside the sweet shop

Moz is flanked by Ding and Henny. They are facing Jeff. A group of bystanders surrounds them.

Moz: You came. *(Triumphant)*

Jeff: Of course I came. *(Jayne enters behind Jeff but stands frozen.)*

Moz: This needn't happen, Jeff, we can talk it over, you keep your mouth shut and there's no problem.

Jeff: It's too late I've talked.

Moz: Tell them it's a lie. Tell them it's a lie or .....

Jeff: You don't understand, do you? It won't work any more. I'm not afraid of you. You're nobody. You, Ding, Henny, you're no-one.

Moz: *(Cross and punches Jeff in stomach.)* Shut up. *(Punch)* Shut up or you're really going to get hurt.

Jeff: But I have been already, any number of times. But this time's different, I'm not afraid, people know what's going on. Every punch just makes it worse. *(He smiles.)* But not for me, for you Morris, for all of you. The more you hit me the more they know. You've lost Morris, I've told the truth, I've stitched you up. *(He shows real amusement.)*

Moz: *(Screams in rage.)* Get him, get him lads. *(Moz is infuriated as he realises the trap. Ding and Henny instead of joining Moz step back. Moz realises he is isolated.)*

Moz: Cowards!

         (Moz attacks Jeff who offers little resistance. The bystanders move in closer but do not attempt to interfere. Only Jayne tries to intervene.)

Jayne: *(Screams)* Stop it please! Can't somebody, stop it?

         As Jayne calls out , Mum, Dad, Neil, Mr Kershaw and Mr Myers arrive. The onlookers step back to allow parents and teachers to surround Moz and Jeff. The cast freeze as if in a tableau and Mum and Mr Myers sing their final song.

Mum's Song

From life's trials we cannot save them,
Despite our love, however deep.
Our dearest love, our child so precious
Is never ours to keep.

As they grow we watch their progress,
Every loss and every gain,
Every step and every stumble,
Every hurt and every pain.

(Continue to duet with Mr Myers)

Duet with Mr Myers

Is it all we can do to cast down our eyes
And pretend that each day we can't hear the cries
Of the frightened, the dying, the lost, the forlorn,
Who, like our own children one day were born to -
A father, a mother who dreamed of so much
And now see their loved one shattered and crushed.
The child they both dreamed of, with fear in its eyes,
Racked with self-doubt, surrounded by lies.
But, like the wise monkeys, with nothing to say,
We stand there in silence while evil holds sway.

And we're all of us guilty we each could do more
To stop the injustice, to make the young sure
That our world can mean more than a miserable place
Where the bully can thrive and spit in your face.
And it starts with the parents with caring and trust
With a kindness to listen, the will to be just,
It starts with self knowledge and ends with the need
To choose truth and freedom, not violence and greed.
But, like the wise monkeys with nothing to say,
We stand there in silence while evil holds sway.

Mum Solo

Try to be there when they need us,
Give them freedom, let them grow.
Teach them trust and teach them kindness,
For the day when they will go.

There's no time for a rehearsal,
The spotlight's on right from the start,
There's no prompter if you stumble,
You just have to play your part.

An anti-bullying project:
Outcomes and Conclusions

Turning Blind Eyes was originally the central focus for a whole school anti-bullying project at Woolston High School, Warrington, Cheshire. The project involved all subject areas, all age groups, parents, governors and outside agencies. The conclusions of the project are summarised here but you can obtain details of how it worked and INSET materials from Carel Press.

The outcome of the project at Woolston High School was entirely positive and continues to show benefit. Ofsted inspectors commented on the benefits of the project and found ample evidence through interviews with pupils and parents of the sense of well being and caring generated within the school.

Woolston High School now has a firmly established anti-bullying policy which enjoys a high profile amongst staff, parents, pupils and the community at large. The project is on-going in that departments have retained schemes of work in their teaching plans and thus the message is passed to new intake pupils and reinforced as they progress through the school.

Primary feeder schools have been made aware of Woolston's stance on bullying and the induction programme for prospective pupils and their parents includes details of anti-bullying policy. All parents receive the school's code of conduct in which they are advised of policy and introduced to the school's philosophy. Additionally, advice is given about how to detect if a child is being bullied, how to proceed, who to contact at school and what to expect in terms of outcome.

Pupils, on entering the school, receive a personal log book. As well as containing timetable details, the booklet contains the school's policy on bullying. It outlines what children should expect from school, how to go about reporting incidents of bullying, who to speak to and what to expect from the system.

The success achieved at Woolston High School owes much to the flexibility of the project. The management and staff were prepared, at every stage, to adapt their thinking as the project unfolded without losing sight of its fundamental principles. The following points emerged as essential to the success of the project and it is recommended that any similar work should include or consider them.

1   Under the Children Act, schools have a duty of care.

2   The project must be seen to have the full support of senior staff; philosophically, financially and educationally.

3   The project should involve as many staff as possible from the outset and ensure that all departments are represented.

4   Money and time should be made available for staff Inset (not just teachers

but office staff, mid-day assistants, technicians, caretakers) from the very beginning, enabling a united and consistent approach from the start.

5 When arranging Inset the co-ordinator should seek the assistance and opinions of a variety of staff to confer ownership.

6 The school should create an atmosphere of openness to ensure that pupils, parents and governors feel comfortable when offering their opinions about policy etc.

7 The school must ensure that it creates a universally acceptable definition of what bullying is. It is important to emphasise that is often the perception of the victim, not the intention of the perpetrator, which is important. 'I didn't mean to...' is not an excuse.

8 Boys and girls can be bullies but their methods may differ.

9 The project is about re-education and prevention, not revenge. Punishment is often only another form of bullying and is really an admission of despair from teachers. We are charged with educating everyone. Where possible, therefore, our priority should be to protect the victim and modify the behaviour of the bully.

10 Pupils want to feel safe and parents want to know that they are safe. Once the problem is brought into the open, a huge amount of support will be forthcoming.

Video

Following on from the success of the project the school was commissioned (by Cheshire County Council) to make an educational video based on a shortened version of the play. The video, which can be used with pupils or as a staff training resource, is also available from Carel Press.

Suggested source material

Organisations

Anti-Bullying Campaign
10 Borough High Street
London SE1 9QQ
Tel: 0171 378 1446

Careline
12 Romney Place
Maidstone ME13 6LE
Telephone counselling for anyone experiencing bullying.

Childline 0800 1111
Freepost 1111
London EC4B 4BB
Office telephone 0171 239 1000

Kidscape
152 Buckingham Palace Road
London
SW1W 9TR
Tel: 0171 730 3300

Parentline
57 Hart Road
Thundersly
Essex SS7 3PD
Tel: 01268 757077
Groups provide support for parents under stress.

Parents Against Bullying
58 Dunmore Avenue
Blackpool
FY3 7QW

The Scottish Council for Research in Education
15 St John Street
Edinburgh EH8 8JR
Tel: 0131 557 2944

Young Minds Trust
22A Boston Place
London NW1 6ER
Tel: 0171 724 7262

Resources

Bullying: don't suffer in silence
Department for Education

Bullying: A Positive Response
(Advice for Parents, Governors & Staff in Schools) by Delwyn Tattum
Learning Resources Centre
Faculty of Education
Cardiff Institute of Higher Education
Cyncoed Road
Cardiff CF2 6DX

Bullying: an annotated bibliography of literature and resources
National Youth Agency
17-23 Albion Street
Leicester LE1 6GD

From Carel Press:

Turning Blind Eyes
Video Package with Teacher's Notes.

Essential Articles 1, 2, 3
Newspaper and magazine articles on bullying, as well as many other topics, including first person accounts from bullies, victims and parents.

Fact File
Annually updated statistics on many subjects including crime, environment, young people.

Original Cast List

Cast:

Abid Ali	Moz
Steven Lythgoe	Ding
Steven Martin	Henny
Nicola Kenny	Janet
Dena Tarry	Jayne
Stephen Ashburner	Jeff
Tim Roberts	Richardson
Joanne Bright	Monica
Helen Healey	Mum
David O'Hanlon	Dad
Phillip Woodward	Neil
Leah Broadstock	Gran
Jeanette Millins	Miss Hardman
Catherine Green	Mrs Myers
Andrew Williams	Mr Kershaw
Claire Lawson	Gillian
Johanne Knight	Joanne
Helen Syms	Angela
Sylvia Robson	Dawn

Bystanders:

Lisa Birchall
Emma Brown
Claire Dykes
Vicky Holding
Kelly Johnson
Kelly O'Neill
Nicola Syms
Ella McDermott
Kate Evans
Louisa Herridge
Katie Hodges
Sarah Lawson
Joanne Mooney
Naomi Taylor
Helen Williams
Jenny Marks
Louise Hare

Production notes

Production details & Music: For reasons of space, only the melody lines of songs are included in this edition. The musical arrangements and more detailed production notes are available in the production pack from Carel Press.

Staging
The original production was staged in a school Arts Theatre, on the floor, with the audience on tiered seating. The wings and backstage areas were formed by the black curtains permanently hung in the theatre. The studio nature of the setting did not lend itself to permanent scenery of the 'Box Set' variety and the large number of scenes required a fluid arrangement to create the settings. The method used is best described as multiple staging. The homes of Morris and Tipman were permanently set and separated by a large video projection screen. There was no attempt at realism in the sense that the sets were not dressed with carpets, curtains, ornaments etc. Only the minimum furniture necessary to demonstrate location was used and this proved to be adequate. Above each home hung a slide projection screen and these were used, with the video, to create an impression of atmosphere and location.
Having used the upstage area (approximately a third) of the acting area for the homes the remaining space was used for school, playground, shop front, discos etc. These areas were established using lighting and a set of specially constructed staging 'blocks'. Two 'blocks' (length 2.5m, height 2m, depth 45cm) were 'trucked' allowing them to be wheeled around the stage to different locations. Four other smaller blocks (length 1.25m, height 60cm, depth 45cm) were carried around the stage as needed. By using these blocks in different configurations acting areas were established to give the required locations. (see ground plan for a suggested configuration).

The Blocks
The boxes, large and small were constructed from 2" x 2" (50mm x 50mm) softwood frames and panelled using ordinary hardboard. The hardboard was nailed on 'rough' side outwards to give a key to the covering and to allow the 'smooth' side to be used for later sets.The larger 'trucks' were strengthened at the corners to allow standard 4" (10cm) bogey wheels to be bolted to them.

Covering the Blocks
All of the blocks were papered using ordinary wallpaper glue and A3 sized photocopies of newspaper headlines. Various headlines relating to the abuse of power were collected and pasted up onto A4. In some cases they were enlarged and repasted. The A4 'masters' (about a dozen in all) were enlarged to A3 and pasted like a collage to the blocks. They were also used to panel around and disguise the stand etc carrying the video projector.
The purpose of this setting technique was to extend and emphasise the premise of the play. The actors, quite literally, were surrounded by examples of

violence, bullying and the abuse of power thus reflecting society in general. For the audience the fact that the headlines were all fairly recent underlined just how much violence and intimidation confronts young people on a daily basis. This idea of a society steeped in violence was further developed in the use of the screens.

The Screens
Throughout the play the two slide screens and the video screen were used in a variety of permutations to establish locations and to support the themes of the play.
At it simplest level a slide above the Tipman household, for example, of an ordinary semi-detached house was used to establish a setting. For the school yard, slides of school buildings could appear on both screens and video of pupils arriving/walking up the drive etc shown on the video screen.
In a more complex way the video, in particular, was used to indicate violence in society. During the family scenes, for example the video screen represented the family television. This served a number of purposes:

1   There was no need for televisions on the set, the family looked into space and the audience saw the images.

2   Time of day could be established with morning news, lunchtime bulletins, evening news etc.

3   On each occasion that we 'visited' one of the houses the television was on covering the scene change, establishing time of day and reporting on some war/crime/pollution/act of terrorism etc from around the world.

When dialogue started the television was 'switched off' as part of the action. In school, in Myers' lessons, video footage of Nazi Germany was used to set the scene.

Finding Film and Video Material
Most of the slides required were taken in and around the school neighbourhood. Several cast members gave permission for their homes to be photographed. Funeral/gravestone photographs were taken in the local cemetery during the weekend when family and friends were not there to be upset. A funeral cortège was videoed by arrangement with a local undertaker who gave permission for his cars to be filmed on the way to pick up mourners. Once again this avoided grief and embarrassment. Other footage was taped directly from the television news, edited together at school and later at a local college. Permission to use footage was obtained readily from BBC News and Current Affairs Marketing. To avoid the problems of synchronisation the video was run without sound and new 'voice overs' recorded and played back as sound cues. By using only film footage as opposed to 'Newscaster to camera' pieces there was no problem with lip synchronisation.

For the newsagent/sweetshop scenes slides were taken outside a local shop. A newspaper 'A' board carrying appropriate headlines was placed in front of the shop and the same board was used 'live' on stage during the scene to tie slides and action together. This material was readily available from local newspaper distributors.

Alternatives
The ways in which any play can be staged are almost infinite. The system described above worked well but can be simplified. Video could be dispensed with and the suggestion of time and events created by radio links. Slides, although on the face of it complicated, are probably worth preserving since they avoid the use of large amounts of scenery. In smaller areas or more permanent proscenium style settings it may be desirable to dispense with the blocks. In such a case it might be an idea to introduce headlines onto backing flats. Not only would this preserve the symbolism of the set it would also allow simplicity of setting in what is normally a realistic stage form. For directors short of space it is possible to use only one 'family' set for both families. This could serve to illustrate that there is not necessarily any great socio-economic difference between bully and victim. Finally, if directors decide to do away with blocks it is useful to have benches as an alternative since they can be used to break up acting areas, are acceptable forms of seating in school yards and are easier to strike than chairs in classroom scenes.

Casting
The style of the play offers an opportunity for the director to give performance opportunities to a large number of children of varied ages. In the case of the main characters there is some scope for variation. It would be possible, for example, for Myers to be played by either a male or a female without altering the sense of the piece.

In the original production, the character of Moz, though originally written for a white actor, was cast as an Asian and his name changed to Moben Ahmed. This decision was taken purely on the basis of talent available and there was no intention to advance theories about bullying based on ethnic considerations. The author is aware that different schools have different needs and that it may be necessary or appropriate to change the race or sex of some characters. However, care should be taken that an overall balance in casting and the integrity of the plot are both maintained. The publishers are prepared to discuss any such issues when application is made for a performance.

Basic Groundplan

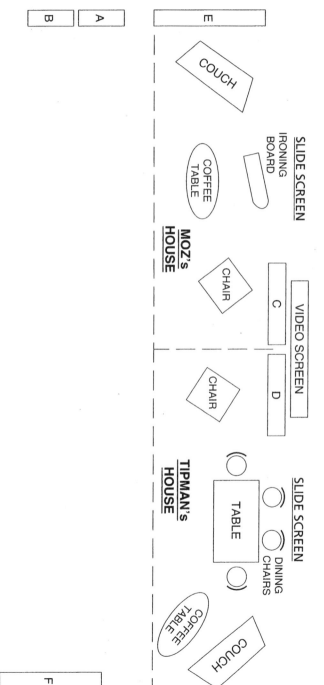

A	B

E

SLIDE SCREEN

COUCH

IRONING BOARD

COFFEE TABLE

MOZ's HOUSE

CHAIR

C

VIDEO SCREEN

CHAIR

D

TIPMAN's HOUSE

SLIDE SCREEN

TABLE

DINING CHAIRS

COFFEE TABLE

COUCH

AUDIENCE

F

Blocks are in storage position here and can be moved into different positions to denote settings. By moving blocks E and F on this setting each household can be obscured or shown separately if the director wishes.

A,B,C,D: Blocks 125 x 60 x45
E,F: Trucks 250 x 200 x 45

Back to school

Mum's song

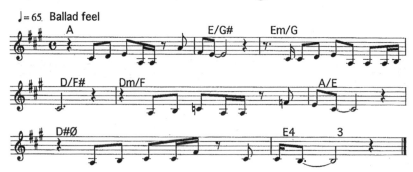

One way to treat the kids

Melody Lines for Songs

Playground songs

Myer's song

Jeff's song

Cool dude rap

Melody Lines for Songs

Gran's song

etc.

Jayne's song